D1639724

ADVENTURE UNDERGROUND

The Story of the World's Great Tunnels

ADVENTURE UNDERGROUND

The Story of the World's Great Tunnels

by

JOSEPH GIES

ILLUSTRATED

LONDON
ROBERT HALE LIMITED
63 Old Brompton Road, S.W.7

First published in Great Britain 1962

PRINTED IN GREAT BRITAIN
BY CLARKE, DOBLE AND BRENDON LIMITED
CATTEDOWN, PLYMOUTH

To the many engineers and the thousands of
tunnel workers who paid with their lives
for our conquest of the river and mountain
barriers of the world, this book is dedicated.

CONTENTS

ILLUSTRATIONS

LINE DRAWINGS

ACKNOWLEDGEMENTS

The above illustrations are copyright by the following: Paul Popper, Nos. 1 and 3; the *Radio Times* Hulton Picture Library, 4, 5, 8, 9, 12 and 19; Culver Service, New York, 6; Camera Press, 7; Brown Brothers, New York, 13, 14, 15, 18 and 23; the London Transport Executive, 16; the Society for Cultural Relations with the U.S.S.R., 17; *Paris Match*, 20 and 21; and the British Travel and Holidays Association, 22.

FOREWORD

This book describes some of the great adventures of tunnel engineers under the rivers and mountains of the world, and foretells those of the future—under the seas. Since I began it as a result of meeting Mr. Frank Davidson and Mr. Cyril C. Means, Jr., president and executive secretary of Technical Studies, Inc., an acknowledgement of their cordial and enlightening help is in order. Not only did Mr. Davidson and Mr. Means supply me with a mass of material, printed and oral, on their own extraordinary project, but Mr. Means was the source of several of the stories about ancient tunnels in Chapter 3.

For the great bulk of the material in the book I am indebted to the American Society of Civil Engineers and the Engineering Societies Library. The liberal policy of Dr. Ralph Phelps, director of the Library, and the co-operation of Mr. M. O. Chenoweth, the Society's Public Relations Director, removed many of the difficulties of assembling the material. I was given free access to the Library's unrivalled collection of tunnelling literature, published and unpublished, and even allowed to carry from the premises several very valuable, if not irreplaceable works. Louis Figuier's treatise on the Mont-Cenis tunnel, for example, is certainly extremely difficult to obtain anywhere —and the copy which I was permitted to borrow from the Engineering Societies was autographed by Professor Daniel Colladon, inventor of the compressed-air system used at Mont-Cenis—a collector's item which I am happy to say I returned unharmed. A glance at the bibliography, ninety per cent of which came from the Engineering Societies' Library, will testify to the role the Library played in the book's preparation.

Finally, one of the Society's distinguished members, Mr. David G. Baillie, F.A.F.C.E., read the manuscript and made several invaluable corrections and suggestions, especially in connection with subaqueous tunnelling in general and compressed-air sickness in particular.

I profited from the assistance of Miss Jane Orth, chief

researcher for *This Week Magazine*. In addition to helping with the research, Miss Orth turned artist and drew the maps and sketches that accompany the text.

Another *This Week* staff member, Mrs. Marianne Tyrrasch, picture researcher, helped in the job of unearthing tunnel art.

Finally, my wife, Frances Carney Gies, contributed importantly in editing and translating. I might also mention my youngest son, Paul, without whose help I certainly would have finished much sooner.

Prologue: Lunch at Lüchow's

One November day in 1956 two young lawyers met for lunch at Lüchow's Restaurant on Fourteenth Street in New York. One, Cyril C. Means, Jr., a former Stanford University law professor, was Arbitration Director of the New York Stock Exchange. The other, Frank P. Davidson, was an attorney with an office on Fifth Avenue. Davidson was just back from a trip to Europe, and like many returning European travellers, recalled most vividly the worst rather than the best episode of his trip. Again, like many returning tourists, the disaster he described was a crossing of the English Channel in rough weather. With his wife and two children he had made the trip from Dover to Ostend by a Channel steamer that seemed to turn over several times *en route*.

Davidson, a Canadian Army veteran of the Second World War, had crossed the Channel before, but this, he asserted, was the worst.

" 'The damned ship lurched and slithered,' eh?" said Means, quoting Rupert Brooke.

Davidson agreed that it had indeed, and added, "My wife will be hard to convince about another Channel crossing unless they build a tunnel under the thing."

A tunnel? Means thought he remembered reading something about a scheme for a Channel tunnel in *Popular Mechanics* when he was a boy.

"I wonder if you really could dig a tunnel there?" Davidson said.

Could you dig a tunnel under the ocean? There were tunnels under rivers, weren't there? The Hudson Tubes under the Hudson River in New York, and the subways there under the East River? Those were pretty short crossings, though, compared with the English Channel.

But Lüchow's is an exceptionally cheerful place for lunch, and presently, perhaps under the influence of a second seidel of dark Löwenbräu Münchener, Means suggested, "Let's just for fun find out about it—see if anybody's ever thought of digging a tunnel under the Channel."

Davidson agreed it would be worth a few dollars to send a girl to the New York Public Library to look into the thing, more or less just for laughs.

When he returned to his office he had his secretary get a free-lance researcher on the telephone. The next morning he felt a trifle foolish when the girl appeared, but doggedly explained to her that he was interested in a tunnel under the English Channel and wanted to know what had been written about the subject. The girl the agency had sent proved to be an exceptionally bright and able young woman. But Davidson's impression, the day after giving her her instructions, was that she was unreliable. The whole day went by and he heard nothing from her. So did the next day. In fact, several weeks passed . . . what in the world was keeping the girl?

Then she came in—bearing a forty-five-page typescript—"Notes on the English Channel Tunnel." When Davidson recovered from his first shock, he settled down to do some reading.

When he finished, he did two things immediately. He called Cyril Means to come quick and read, and he hired the girl researcher, Mrs. Joan Reiter, on a permanent basis. She was obviously a highly competent researcher, and Davidson suddenly had the feeling he was going to be able to use a researcher for quite a little while.

The story Mrs. Reiter told in her notes was certainly one to stir all sorts of ideas—besides being utterly absorbing.

The whole thing started, it seemed, with Napoleon. . . .

CHAPTER ONE

How Colonel Blimp Saved England from Napoleon

The fact that the first proposal for a tunnel under the English Channel came from a French engineer in the time of Napoleon was a most unhappy irony. The year was 1802, the interval of the Peace of Amiens; Napoleon was First Consul. The Engineer was Albert Mathieu, who had driven shafts and tunnels in coal mines and who lived near the Channel coast. His idea was obviously taken seriously, for it was carried all the way to Napoleon himself. Mathieu's plan was based on knowledge of the topography—but not the geology—of the tunnel floor; he proposed headings from either shore to meet at the Varne Bank, a ridge which rises in the middle of the Straits of Dover to within fifteen feet of the surface at low tide. In the visionary spirit of his age, Mathieu proposed raising the Varne Bank to an artificial island which would serve as a staging post; the horses which drew the carriages and wagons through the tunnel would need to come up at this point for a breather. They would certainly need it, for Mathieu's tunnel would be illuminated by gas. With several thousand horses and passengers in a thirty-mile tunnel, the atmosphere would be fairly appalling, even without the burning gas.

Napoleon is said to have been interested, but the whole idea was dropped with the approach of fresh war clouds. This is an interesting point, as will be seen later.

The second Channel Tunnel scheme was proposed in England in 1803; it came from an Englishman named Mottray who suggested that segments of iron tubing should be laid across the Channel floor, whose ridges would be trenched to provide an even bed. This was a really remarkable idea; the underwater trench method of tunnelling was not to become a practical reality for a hundred years.

The resumption of the Napoleonic wars not only ended contemporary speculation about a tunnel; it cast a permanent shadow over the idea. For Napoleon's Grand Army, gathered at Boulogne in 1805, though eventually launched across the Rhine rather than across the Channel, left a memory in Britain that time could scarcely efface. Moreover, as tunnelling began to grow into a science, the hazards of the project began to have a sobering effect. What was the bottom of the Channel made of, anyway? Was it really chalk all the way across? Could chalk sustain the enormous pressure of the ocean? Would it hold out water?

But in the 1840s a brilliant and indefatigable dreamer commenced the studies that were to turn the highly visionary scheme of a channel tunnel into a practical engineering possibility. This man, Thomé de Gamond, came from a wealthy family and acquired an excellent education not only in mine engineering but in medicine and law. He became so fascinated by the idea of a Channel crossing that he spent his whole life, as well as his family fortune, in pursuing it. His earliest schemes were chimerical; a tube to be laid across the Channel floor, like that of Mottray; various wholly impractical bridges; a concrete ferry boat operating between two moles; a viaduct carried on granite arches.

In 1856 de Gamond, reverting to a tunnel, succeeded in placing his idea before Napoleon III, nephew of the great Bonaparte. This plan called for a stone-lined tunnel large enough for two rail tracks, from Cape Gris-Nez to a point between Dover and Folkestone. Like Mathieu, de Gamond wished to crown the Varne Bank with an artificial island, a sort of halfway house open to shipping. Napoleon III, always interested in humanitarian and scientific schemes, referred the tunnel to a Scientific Research Commission, which reported cautiously but favourably.

Napoleon III's interest was a turning point. The French ambassador in London, the Duc de Persigny, an old comrade of the Emperor, became interested; so did Michel Chevalier, the leading French economist of the day and strong promoter of Anglo-French commercial relations. French interest communicated itself across the Channel; Prince Albert was enthusiastic. Unfortunately political events suddenly chilled this growing atmosphere of cordiality towards the tunnel. On January 14, 1858, an Italian patriot, Felice Orsini, attempted, for complicated reasons, to assassinate Napoleon III, and for even more complicated reasons, the result was a quarrel between France and Britain. The tunnel was shelved.

It was very far from forgotten, however. Several new projects for bridges and tunnels appeared in the next few years, of which by far the most notable was de Gamond's newest—his seventh—scheme, and prepared with the collaboration of a British mining engineer named William Low, presented at the great Paris Exposition of 1867. Once more the interest of both French and British governments was enlisted; once more political events, this time in the shape of the Franco-Prussian War of 1870, temporarily intervened.

The de Gamond-Low plan called for two separate tubes; another British engineer of great distinction, Sir John Hawkshaw, now proposed a single tunnel with two tracks, on a somewhat different route. Sir John's plan suddenly moved to the fore in 1872, when it was adopted as the official project of the newly formed English Channel Tunnel Company, which applied to the British Board of Trade for permission to start digging. The following year the Anglo-French Submarine Railway Company was formed, with the object of digging the de Gamond-Low tunnel. The most illustrious British engineers, including Isambard Brunel, son of the Thames tunnel digger, supported one or the other of the rival projects. Queen Victoria's government, headed by William E. Gladstone, took an active interest; through its ambassador the government of the new French Republic was formally notified of Britain's interest.

At this moment the Gladstone government fell and was replaced by Benjamin Disraeli and the Tories. The French government then took a diplomatic sounding, spelling out the terms under which it was prepared to sanction the tunnel. These included a ninety-nine-year concession to the French and British tunnel companies.

The question was now referred to the British Board of Trade, while a bill was introduced in Parliament for concession of land for the tunnel portal. The Board of Trade reacted favourably, in a memorandum which noted in reservation only that the question of how the French and British companies were to co-operate would have to be arranged, and that "military necessities" would require a means of stopping traffic through the tunnel. The Board of Trade even wondered if "the right

B

to exercise the power" should not be exercised "without claim for compensation."

Lord Derby, the Prime Minister, informed the French government in December of 1874 that Her Majesty's present Government, like its predecessor, favoured the tunnel and, furthermore, that it approved of the steps taken and proposed. Meantime in France a French Channel Tunnel Company, backed by the North Railway and headed by Michel Chevalier, was formed. In August of 1875 acts were passed by both the French Assembly and the British Parliament authorizing the acquisition of land by the two tunnel companies. It seemed as if the hour of the Channel Tunnel had struck.

The route which Hawkshaw and his French colleagues had selected ran from the French coast north of Sangatte to St. Margaret's Bay, just east of Dover. Soundings indicated that grey chalk, soft but firm and impervious to water, extended the entire distance at the chosen depth of 127 metres. In 1875-76 the French Company took thousands of soundings and made a deep boring near Sangatte. It also experimented with the grey chalk and found it to be plastic, and capable of withstanding considerable shocks. At the same time an important advance was made on the political front; an Anglo-French Commission signed a protocol designed as the basis of a treaty. The companies were given five years to conclude a working agreement, twenty years to build the tunnel, and a monopoly for ninety-nine years. The question of defensive fortifications and interruption of traffic in wartime was also touched on, but in what proved to be a very inadequate way.

The French company now set industriously to work on the preliminary shaft, which was sunk to a depth of eighty-six metres (282 feet), passing through the water-bearing strata and penetrating well into the impervious grey chalk. A second, larger shaft was then sunk, to serve for drainage when the main heading was commenced. Pumps, workshops, air compressors, and all the complex paraphernalia of tunnelling sprang up around the new workings. From the large shaft a small pilot gallery was driven, curving in a north-east direction to pass around a pocket of dubious rock. The gallery gave virtually final confirmation to the engineers' sanguine hopes: water seepage was negligible in the grey chalk, and the "fault rock" could be bypassed without peril. The impermability of the grey chalk was of a significance highly appreciated in this era when compressed-air tunnelling was being born. The Channel was 180 feet deep at its deepest point, nearly thrice the depth of the Hudson River, where sandhogs were pioneering dangerously at this very time. If compressed air had to be used to balance the tremendous water pressure of the English Channel, no workman could live in it.

In Britain, meanwhile, several years passed with little activity; the British company which had adopted Hawkshaw's tunnel plan was unable to raise money to begin work. In consequence William Low, the collaborator of de Gamond, who had died in 1876, sought backing for his own and de Gamond's plan. He obtained it from Sir Edward Watkin, one of Britain's greatest rail tycoons, chairman of the South Eastern Railway Company, which operated the coastal line into Dover and Folkestone.

Sir Edward was already a tunnel enthusiast, and he lost no time in seizing the opportunity offered, getting a new act passed by Parliament authorizing purchase of land by his company, and having £20,000 voted by his board of directors for the preliminary work. Since the older company still held title to the land on St. Margaret's Bay, Sir Edward and Low picked a point west of Dover, at Abbots Cliff and Shakespeare Cliff, for their work. Drawing on the experience already gained by the French at Sangatte, Low sank two shafts, one on either cliff, and began boring his pilot heading out under the Channel.

The French had been pushing their gallery at Sangatte by the rock-tunnelling method of drilling and blasting. But this technique was not only dangerous, it failed to take advantage of the softness of the chalk. The British wondered if it would not be possible to realize a dream of several contemporary engineers by designing a machine which would bore a full gallery without the use of explosives. They tried out two, and the second, the creation of a military engineer named Colonel Beaumont, who had helped build the fortifications at Dover, worked to perfection. It consisted of a rotating shaft with a propeller-like blade seven feet wide. The blade had teeth, fixed at a slight angle to dig into the material in front. Compressed air was the motive power, with the felicitous advantage of ventilating the heading while it operated. The chalk detritus was carried by a belt of buckets to the rear and automatically dumped in a waiting car. Slater and Barnett, the chief biographers of the Channel Tunnel, accurately describe the Beaumont machine as "a splendid piece of Victorian ingenuity." The French promptly adopted an impoved model for their Sangatte heading.

Through 1880 and into 1881 the Channel Tunnel gave every outward sign of being one of the great promotional and engineering successes of all time. Sir Edward Watkin organized a new company with a capital of £250,000, and invited parties of influential visitors to luncheons under the sea. Stock in both British and French companies shot up in the market. The redoubtable Beaumont drill bored out from Sangatte and Shakespeare Cliff hundreds of feet a week.

But before the end of 1881 an opposition, at first insufficiently taken into account, suddenly grew in force to the point where it was recognized, too late, as a major threat to the tunnel. This opposition was from the British War Office. Americans, taught in school that Britain was the great world power of its day, are hardly aware of the apprehension with which an invasion from France was regarded in Britain throughout the nineteenth century. The spectre of Napoleon, who had been barely turned aside from an invasion of England by the most strenuous diplomatic and financial exertions, haunted the island for generations. We have noted the profound irony that Napoleon had dropped the first tunnel scheme precisely because he was going to war with England.

Relations between the two countries had been friendly since Waterloo; through most of the period they had actually been allies. Yet the Duke of Wellington opposed building a railway to Portsmouth in the 1840s on the grounds that it would facilitate a French invasion. Now in the 1880s all the leading British generals spoke out against the tunnel. Sir Garnet Wolseley, the Adjutant-General, asserted that the completion of the tunnel would impose conscription on the British people, and even with the creation of a powerful land army, he was by no means satisfied that Britain would be safe. "Our end [of the tunnel] may be seized by surprise and treachery without any warning and before the machinery designed for its destruction had been put in motion . . . to seize our end of the tunnel . . . would be a very small military operation."

His Royal Highness the Duke of Cambridge, Field-Marshal

and commander-in-chief of the army, strongly seconded Wolseley's views, in a memorandum to the Cabinet. So did General Sir Lintorn Simmons in a public communication. Answering the argument that the tunnel could be rendered useless by flooding, he pointed out that "it is not to be believed that a great country like France could not find the means for reopening it for traffic within a reasonable time." And the general concluded: "On a careful consideration of the whole question it is inconceivable that any Government in England can entertain for a moment a proposal that, by destroying our perfect insularity, will make a breach in the natural defence of our island fortress—a defence for which we cannot be too grateful to a merciful Providence."

For the tunnel companies, Colonel Beaumont undertook to reply. His answer to the invasion fears was reasoned and just. He pointed out that Dover, whose fortifications he himself had helped construct, was a first-class fortress; that the tunnel portal would be under its guns; that arrangements could easily be made to flood the tunnel; that these arrangements could be kept secret and under the sole control of the Dover commandant. He disposed of the idea of a small force seizing the portal by a *coup de main*; it was inconceivable that such a force could traverse the tunnel without being detected. As for the question of flooding, Colonel Beaumont suggested the simple and effective expedient of mains laid from the sea, under the Dover fortifications, into the tunnel. In case of emergency the Dover commandant, or any subordinate, could unlock the main and flood the tunnel on a moment's notice.

On their side the French made an extraordinary effort to reassure. They offered to construct the approach at Sangatte in such a way that the line would emerge in a loop on the naked coastal cliff before plunging under the sea; thus providing the British fleet with an unmissable target.

But the generals gained swift support. The *London Times* arrayed itself against the tunnel; of possibly even more weight, Queen Victoria thought it "very objectionable." A Parliamentary commission reported that no measures for closure of the tunnel in time of war could be relied upon completely. The rest of the Press, London, provincial and Scottish, joined the *Times*. Poet Laureate Alfred Lord Tennyson, fellow poet Robert Browning, philosophers Thomas Henry Huxley and

Herbert Spencer and various other luminaries declared themselves in opposition. A new committee of Parliament made a fresh investigation and after questioning a great number of witnesses, mostly hostile to the tunnel, recommended that the government refuse its sanction to the enterprise. With this decision, the tunnel was killed.

Present-day British writers, such as Slater and Barnett, wax sarcastic over the grounds on which this great enterprise was postponed for three-quarters of a century at enormous cost. Certainly the Duke of Cambridge, Sir Garnet Wolseley, and the other generals strike an attitude dangerously reminiscent of Gilbert and Sullivan characters, while Colonel Beaumont, with his rational arguments and his ingenious machine, as certainly represents the healthy best of the Victorian tradition. Yet something must be said for Britain's military alarmists. A tunnel could not, contrary to what Sir Garnet Wolseley pretended or imagined, be used as a primary means of attack on the island of Britain. But indisputably it could be used to support a seaborne invasion. If a Continental power made a sudden attack, seizing a broad area of the south-east British coast, before the British Navy could effectively intervene, the tunnel, even though it were flooded on the first day of hostilities, could be a decisive factor. Interestingly enough, the Duke of Cambridge foresaw the possibility of an attack from another quarter besides France: "Any power . . . which, when at war with France, had taken possession of Belguim, would find it possible to seize Calais, and might find it convenient even to punish an alliance of ours with France, by a sudden seizure of Dover."

Looking back with the advantage of hindsight knowledge of two World Wars and the detachment of a non-British observer, one may be struck by two surprising aspects of the great tunnel controversy of 1882. First, it seems curiously out of character for soldiers to argue in opposition to a project whose chief military objection would be that it would impose the necessity of a stronger army. It would be hard to find a parallel to this picture of field-marshals and generals raising trembling forefingers to conjure up the spectre of conscription and taxes. Certainly Colonel Blimp is an odd sort of superpatriot.

The other surprising element in the fiasco of 1882 is the failure of the tunnellers to seek adequate and realistic answers for the military objection. Measures for flooding the tunnel were not enough; the French proposal to build a loop track on the Sangatte cliff was not enough; the theoretical, though perfectly valid, proof that a large body of troops could not possibly debouch from the narrow portal under fire was not enough. What was required was an arrangement by which the tunnel could be rendered completely and permanently useless in case of war. In the conditions of 1882 this meant not flooding but demolition, certainly a radical solution and one not likely to appeal to tunnel promoters.

In the absence of such an absolute guarantee against the threat to British insularity, the Channel Tunnel was dealt an all-but-mortal blow—infected with a sort of lingering illness from which it did not recover for upward of seventy years.

At the same time, the 1881-82 work was actually decisive in a favourable sense. Though the tunnel's completion was indefinitely postponed, the enterprise's character was transformed from the hypothetical to the indisputably practical. No one, after the demonstration of Colonel Beaumont's boring machine, could possibly deny the feasibility, in fact, the ease, with which a tunnel could be bored under the English Channel. Thomé de Gamond and the other tunnel theorists had been brilliantly vindicated.

CHAPTER TWO

Colonel Blimp Surrenders

The Parliamentary decision of 1882 did not put an end to discussion. The need for a better means of crossing the Channel naturally did not diminish, and in fact augmented with passing years. An extremely complex scheme was put forward in Britain for train-carrying ferries operating from docks with enormous hydraulic lifts to meet the problem of the Channel's fifteen-foot tides. A French proposal for a bridge mounted on stupendous masonry piers was vetoed by the French Ministry of Marine as creating a "most serious obstacle to navigation"—as it undoubtedly would have. For the first time an American became interested; an inventor named Zerah Colbourn advanced a novel proposal for a tunnel made of sections of steel tube suspended and anchored at a sufficient depth not to interfere with navigation. One advantage of Colbourn's highly impractical scheme was that it would have answered the objections of the War Office—all that would have been necessary in time of war would be to cut the cables and let the tunnel drift off into the North Sea.

In 1890 Sir Edward Watkin, with the backing of Gladstone, now Prime Minister, reopened the debate in the original tunnel project, but the motion was again defeated in Commons. For a dozen years after the question was not raised; Anglo-French colonial rivalry led the two nations dangerously close to war in 1898. Sir Garnet Wolseley, now Field-Marshal Lord Wolseley, commander-in-chief of British forces, must have congratulated himself on his foresight sixteen years earlier; one can well imagine the alarm in Britain had the tunnel been in existence.

But the Fashoda crisis passed and Anglo-French diplomacy successfully partitioned Africa, in the face of German opposition. The result was a new cross-Channel alliance, the Entente Cordiale, and under its Edwardian glow the tunnel project blossomed once more. André Sartiaux and Sir Francis Fox, two leading railroad engineers of their respective countries, were engaged to re-examine the scheme; in doing so they made an important contribution, the substitution of electric for steam locomotives. This change would make construction of the tunnel easier, because electric locomotives can negotiate steeper grades and sharper curves than steam, and consequently the tunnel could be made to dip and twist to stay inside the critical vein of grey chalk. Sartiaux and Fox also made important contributions to solving the drainage problem. The cost of the tunnel was now put at £16,000,000—some four times as high as twenty-five years earlier.

A bill was once more introduced in Parliament, and the debate that followed was very distinctly affected by the changes in the diplomatic line-up. First of all, the French entered directly into the public discussion, by means of a book written under the sponsorship of the French Tunnel Company and with the assistance of the French General Staff. The writer, Georges Viernot, described what happened when he asked senior members of the general staff how England could be invaded via the tunnel by a force of 150,000 men. The G-4 was summoned, and the question put:

"How would you transport 150,000 men by the tunnel from Wissant to Dover?"

The G-4 considered carefully and replied:

"*Mon General,* 150,000 men; that means four army corps or 560 trains. At the rate of forty trains a day, it would call for a period of fifteen days, or three and a half days per corps . . . on condition, that is, that everything was properly co-ordinated with the English authorities and that the detraining stations had been carefully allocated and prepared."

The officer was informed that the hypothetical question was based on the supposition of an invasion of England, and that consequently there would be no question of co-operation with the British.

The G-4 flung up his hands; in the ensuing discussion all the officers in the room came to the unanimous conclusion that since surprise was out of the question at Dover, the problem was not only difficult, it was impossible.

Viernot demolished the arguments of Lord Wolseley, who had very erroneously stated that twenty thousand men could debouch from the portal in four hours. He also pointed out that electric traction would stop at the portal and consequently trains carrying troops could advance no farther till steam engines were attached. In truth, a direct invasion by way of the tunnel was even more unthinkable in 1906 than it had been in 1882, because military equipment was much more massive and complex.

"In all truth," was the conclusion of the French General Staff as recorded by Viernot, "we give up trying to understand how any competent man of good faith and sound judgment could have any doubt as to the fatal results of trying to invade England by the Channel Tunnel."

Of even more significance perhaps was the entrance of the British Navy into the tunnel question for the very first time. Vice-Admiral Sir Charles Campbell declared that the tunnel would be of enormous strategic value—it would provide Britain with excellent communications in wartime and it would enable the Navy to concentrate on blockading the enemy's fleet and destroying his commerce. Very evidently Admiral Campbell was thinking of war with Germany, with which Britain was carrying on a breakneck naval race.

Even some generals spoke up in favour of the tunnel. The military plans of the Entente Cordiale involved British participation in ground warfare on the Continent. A British Expeditionary Force of six divisions plus cavalry was to be kept stationed in England ready to land the moment Belgium was invaded. A Channel Tunnel obviously would enormously facilitate the operation and provide a secure supply system.

But the orthodox military group spoke in the person of a Major-General Sir Frederick Maurice. Sir Frederick denied that adequate precautions could be taken to secure Dover against a surprise attack, or that machinery for flooding could be relied on. Like his predecessors of the '80s, Sir Frederick sounded curiously unlike a general; he warned against the danger to English liberty of a conscription law which he foresaw resulting from the tunnel: "Abroad every detail of daily life is regulated by authority, so far as it may be necessary for purposes of national security."

In January 1907 the British War Office officially declared against the bill. The government promptly recommended rejection and the bill was withdrawn. "The War Office," say Slater and Barnett, "had condemned another generation to seasickness."

In 1913 the tunnellers returned to the charge, this time with support of a newly formed committee in Parliament and a popular daily newspaper. But "the Committee of Imperial Defence was true to the glorious traditions handed down to them by Lord Wolseley and the Duke of Cambridge." In July 1914, two weeks before the outbreak of the First World War, the decision was once more made against the tunnel.

The war came and passed, leaving Europe shaken to its foundations. In France and Britain, victorious at appalling cost, the Armistice atmosphere was a sort of false dawn of pathetic hope. In it the tunnel was again proposed, and on the French side two important events took place. One was on the engineering level; Philippe Fougerolles solved a difficult though not critical problem, that of disposing of the detritus without undue loss of time when the borings achieved considerable length. Fougerolles's idea was to mix the chalk with sea water, a feasible operation, and pump it out into the sea through shafts bored for the purpose. The other event was political. A special committee appointed to examine the legal rights of the forty-year-old French Channel Company pronounced them perfectly valid for an indefinite period. Thus on the French side promoters and investors could act with security.

Furthermore, the French produced a formidable propagandist for the tunnel: Marshal Foch. "If there had been a tunnel under the Channel before the war," said the victor of the Second Marne, "it could have prevented war." And he added, "If the English and the French had had a tunnel under the Channel in 1914, the war would have been shortened by at least two years." With all respect to Marshal Foch, some slight reservations may be made in favour of Colonel Blimp. The tunnel might indeed have given the German government pause in July 1914, but it is too much to say it would have prevented war. And the First Battle of the Marne was a hair-breadth victory; had the Germans won it the destruction of the French and British armies would have been inevitable. The Germans would have been in the same military position they later achieved in 1940, but with a much stronger fleet. In the circumstances the tunnel would at least have represented a considerable potential value to Britain's enemy.

But all that is mere hypothesis; in actual fact, as Sir Arthur Fell, the new leading British proponent of the tunnel, zealously pointed out, German generals and statesmen before the war had regarded the tunnel with distinct distaste both from the military and commercial viewpoints. The British War Office itself was now on record as favouring the tunnel; engineers had been consulted during the war to ascertain whether it could be built swiftly enough to provide a U-boat-proof communications line to France.

But alas for consistency; as soon as the war was over the generals recanted and would have no more of the tunnel. And despite arguments to the effect that the tunnel would provide an ideal public-works programme for the numerous unemployed in Britain in the 1920s, the Labour government, in theory pledged to support the tunnel, objected on grounds of cost.

The result was not so much a defeat as a postponement; for although the military objections of Lord Wolseley and the Duke of Cambridge were actually by no means invalidated by the experience of 1914-18, they seemed to be. At the same time, though the commercial advantages of the tunnel might be said to have dwindled with Britain's diminishing export trade, actually they loomed larger in a more economically minded age. In 1929-30 a new Parliamentary Committee made an exhaustive study and report on all possible methods of creating an effective crossing. A ferry service capable of carrying whole trains in single units was found to be impracticable; the ports on the Continental side could not take ships of the requisite draught, quite apart from the matter of coping with tides, which ran to twenty-one feet at Calais. A bridge project, the carefully thought-out work of two eminent engineers from either side of the Channel, was likewise rejected because of its high cost—£75,000,000—and its danger to navigation. The Committee noted that outside the two three-mile limits, it would be necessary to get the permission of all the maritime nations of the world—an extremely doubtful proposition.

The tunnel again came to the fore. The company's current proposition was twin rail tubes with diameters of eighteen and a half feet plus a seven-foot drainage tunnel. The French company volunteered to undertake alone the preliminary work, including research on the Fougerolles method of removing detritus, provided only they were assured that operations would not be stopped at a later stage.

The Parliamentary investigation of 1930 was sincere and intensive. It penetrated deeply into technical questions—fissures, infilled valleys, the effectiveness of cement-grouting under pressure (as at Tanna and elsewhere) and of the new freezing technique. The consulting engineers came up with a new schedule for the whole project; they suggested driving and lining a pilot tunnel and a drainage tunnel, requiring five years' effort, but reducing the main tunnel's work to three years. Cost: about £30,000,000.

Several analyses of the economic potential of the tunnel were submitted by the interested parties. The Parliamentary Committee, making its own study, reckoned passenger traffic at about three and a third million a year—enough to insure an adequate income.

The Committee also went into the question of "goods," i.e., freight, and its conclusions were less optimistic. A questionnaire submitted to Chambers of Commerce in the various British cities drew "cautious and unenthusiastic" replies. The general view of British industry, surprisingly enough, seemed to be that the rail tunnel would facilitate foreign compeition with domestic manufactures in Britain without affording corresponding advantages to British goods abroad.

The Committee's final conclusion was that "the advantages that would accrue to this country from a Channel Tunnel would be likely to increase with the passage of the years. . ." and that if the Channel Tunnel Company could keep its rates within those already charged for cross-Channel traffic, the project would be worth-while.

But alas for Parliamentary Committees and exhaustive studies; the Imperial Defence Committee, Britain's new highest military board, met again in May 1930, and once more the Channel Tunnel was rejected. After a lively debate, the House of Commons then voted down the Tunnel by 179 to 172; among the aye votes recorded were those of Mr. Winston Churchill and Mr. Aneurin Bevan.

This victory might be described as Colonel Blimp's last stand. Never again was an adverse motion carried in the House of Commons. Yet the tunnel was a long way from being built—over thirty years in fact. The delay since 1930 can be ascribed only in small part to the military objections. More significant were these factors:

1. The world depression and the consequent reluctance of

the British Government to embark on an expensive project (Britain's Depression government was motivated by a far more conservative spirit than the New Deal in the U.S.).

2. A new technical question: the feasibility of a vehicular tunnel. Since a vehicular would require ventilation, a whole new route was needed, one which passed under the Varne and Colbart Banks, two eminences in the Channel floor. The impetus for a vehicular tunnel, and later for a combined road-and-rail tunnel, came from French engineers and government officials.

3. The Second World War, which provided a six-year interruption of all tunnel discussion.

4. A series of improvements in Channel crossings after the war. In 1947 a car ferry service was introduced, though it had the inconvenience of requiring crane-lifting at Dover. In 1948 an air ferry service began carrying cars across the Channel. In 1952 a complete drive-on, drive-off car-ferry service was inaugurated. In the next few years the air-ferry service was greatly augmented.

Yet the multiplication of means for crossing the Channel, and especially for transporting automobiles across it, was actually less a solution of a problem than a symptom of one. Pressure for a tunnel was actually stronger than ever. . . . But what did the British War Office think now?

The experience of 1940 had been dramatic, but strangely inconclusive. Had the tunnel existed could the Germans have invaded Britain by way of it? Not unless they had seized both portals early in the game by parachute drops. Would this have been possible? It seems virtually inconceivable, given the relatively light weapons of parachute troops and the heavy concentration of flak and other arms that surely would have been provided at the portals. But after Hitler's occupation of the European coast, might he have invaded England and then made use of the tunnel for reinforcements and supplies? By that time, surely, the tunnel would have been utterly demolished behind the retreating B.E.F. which, itself, could have used the tunnel to save its equipment.

But two other wartime developments rendered all discussion academic: the atomic bomb and the V-2. The moment it became possible to hit Britain with a weapon carrying total destruction from a distance of a hundred miles or more, the calculations of Lord Wolseley were swept into the limbo of Victorian debris.

In the 1950s the new French tunnel fanatic, André Basdevant, came forward with an idea for a magnificent and modern tunnel, of huge diameter, to carry both auto and rail traffic. Basdevant took his plan not to the French Assembly or to the British Parliament, but to an American General, Alfred M. Gruenther, commanding officer of Allied forces in Europe. Gruenther ordered a study; the report was enthusiastically affirmative. The tunnel would be a strategic advantage for the N.A.T.O. allies.

In February 1955 a question was raised in the House of Commons about the tunnel. In the course of the short debate that followed, an M.P. who favoured the tunnel inquired to what extent "strategic considerations" still prevented the tunnel's construction.

The reply was given by the Minister of Defence: "Scarcely at all." It was the surrender of Colonel Blimp.

Interestingly enough, this minister was the Right Honourable Harold Macmillan.

Frank Davidson was a thoughtful man as he finished Mrs. Reiter's notes.

The thing was fantastic, but it seemed as if a tunnel under the English Channel really was perfectly feasible. They'd even started digging it once.

Of course it was possible that those old engineers of eighty years ago had been mistaken. Maybe it wouldn't be so easy at that. After all, it *was* under the ocean. Wouldn't the workmen get the bends? And there must be an economic aspect to the thing. What would it cost to dig a tunnel all the way from France to England? Would it pay off?

How about other tunnels? How did they work? How had they been dug, anyway? There were tunnels under the Hudson and a lot of other rivers, Davidson knew, and there were tunnels in the Alps. How did you dig tunnels, anyway? And why? When was a tunnel a good idea? What was tunnelling all about, anyway?

Since that day Frank Davidson and his colleague Cyril Means have learned a great deal about tunnelling, and either of them will tell you there are few things more fascinating. . . .

CHAPTER THREE

Men Start Digging

Natural tunnels—caves—were of course an essential part of the life of Paleolithic and Neolithic man. Doubtless he sometimes dug them himself where it was possible, though soft-earth hillsides suitable for cave-digging are not very common. Digging in rock would have been out of the question for men whose tools were themselves made of rock.

But very early in ancient historic times the art of tunnelling was invented. The ancients must have run up against the same double-edged paradox that modern tunnellers have constantly confronted: where tunnelling is easy, it is rarely necessary; where it is necessary it is rarely easy. The earth's crust consists of soil and rock; soil is easy to dig through, but since it is found at low altitudes it rarely provides the ground a tunneller must work. Mountains are made of rock.

Yet occasionally ancient man found soft-ground tunnelling worth-while. Tunnels then as now could serve many different purposes. Then as now a tunnel might be an aqueduct. Here is an example of extraordinary antiquity and authenticity:

King Hezekiah's Aqueduct

In the eighth century B.C., when Assyria was a powerful empire whose heavy hand had already been felt by the lost Ten Tribes of Israel, the little kingdom of Judea looked with apprehension to the possibility of a siege of Jerusalem. The city's water supply lay in a well outside the walls. For reasons which are not altogether clear to archaeologists or Bible exegetes, King Hezekiah resolved to safeguard the city's water supply in a curiously roundabout way. He dug a tunnel which ran from the well in a wide curve, under the city's walls, to the Pool of Siloam, which had formerly lain outside the walls but was now taken inside by a new fortification. Whether the secret aqueduct ever served in time of war is not known.

The distance was only a few hundred feet, and the ground

The Alps, a challenge to tunnellers for centuries, are now being pierced by modern techniques. A historic photograph of the new three-and-a-half-mile long Great Saint Bernard Tunnel linking Italy to Switzerland, showing the meeting of Italian and Swiss mining parties under the Mont-Blanc Massif on April 9, 1962

(Left) A Roman tunnel contemporary with Christ. This "crypta", about two-thirds of a mile long, was driven by the engineer Cocceius in the region of Baiae, near Naples. There is excellent sun lighting through the oblique shaft

(Below) The opening of the Simplon Tunnel in May 1906. Twelve and a half miles under the Alps, this Italo-Swiss engineering feat remains the longest transportation tunnel to this day

was of course soft. But the ancient peoples were, amazingly, capable of hard-rock tunnelling, too. An excellent example is described by Herodotus as "one of the greatest works to be seen in any Greek land," and dates to the seventh century B.C.

Samos Tunnels through Solid Rock

This truly remarkable work was "a double-mouthed channel pierced . . . through the base of a high hill; the whole channel is seven furlongs long, eight feet high and eight feet wide; and throughout the whole of its length there runs another channel twenty cubits deep and three feet wide through which the water coming from an abundant spring is carried by its pipes to the city of Samos. The designer of this work was Eupalinos, son of Naustrophos, a Megarian." This tunnel was discovered by modern archaelogists in 1881. A passage, six feet in diameter, it runs for over 3,000 feet through the limestone rock of a mountain some 900 feet in height. Construction of it, with hammer and chisel, must have taken decades.

Yet the Samos tunnel is almost as remarkable for its planning as for its execution, for it was dug from two headings to meet under the mountain, an extremely difficult calculation. The two headings came very close to meeting; in the end, the workmen in one passage, guided by the sound of hammers in the other, made a right-angle turn, then curved back in an S to make the connection.

Thus the ancients did both soft-ground and hard-rock tunnelling. More fantastic than this is that they are reported to have constructed at least one subaqueous tunnel—certainly the world's first, if the story is true.

Semiramis Tunnels under the Euphrates

This story is vouched for only by an obscure Greek writer of a much later date, and contains certain contradictions. Nonetheless, it is perfectly plausible, and makes a wonderful tunnel riddle. How did Semiramis, Queen of Babylon, build a tunnel under the Euphrates connecting her palace with the Temple of Marduk?

If you know anything about the Euphrates River, the answer should not be difficult. This famous stream dwindles to a muddy trickle in the winter. The queen's engineers first dug a new channel, then diverted the water from its course, then dug a huge trench in the dry river-bed. Meantime the brickmakers, whose art played so important a role in Babylon, were spreading their bricks by the thousands to dry. The trench completed, walls, floor, and arched roof were built in the trench, the whole vast work finished in time for the spring floods. As the waters of Babylon rolled overhead, Queen Semiramis walked dry-shod from her royal residence to worship the Great Marduk in his temple.

To appreciate this wonder of the ancient world, one must realize that it was not until the nineteenth century of the Christian era that another subaqueous tunnel was built!

It is true that certain reservations must be made about it. Diodorus puts the date of the tunnel at the twenty-second century B.C., a time when Babylon was indeed flourishing and Marduk was worshipped. But Queen Semiramis was actually an Assyrian queen of the eighth century, and the Assyrian conquerors of Babylon relegated Marduk to a secondary place in their cosmology. Any Semiramis who ruled at the earlier date is wholly legendary. No archaeological expedition has succeeded in recovering traces of the tunnel, though this is probably understandable enough in view of the changes in the river's course since ancient times.

We must put down Semiramis's tunnel as a dubious marvel. But some very early tunnels by other ancient peoples are thoroughly authentic; the tunnels are still in existence, and it is largely through the tunnels we know about the civilizations that created them.

Tunnels for Dead Pharaohs

Though not true tunnels, in the sense of passages with two terminal portals, the tombs of the Pharaohs and nobles of Egypt are certainly worth mentioning. Breasted describes those of the Empire (1580-1150 B.C.) as "vast galleries, pierced into the mountain, passing from hall to hall, terminating many hundreds of feet from the entrance in a large chamber, where the body of the king is laid in a huge sarcophagus." The elaborate and lengthy tunnel, with its many descending stairways, may have been meant to symbolize the passages of the underworld through which the Egyptians believed the sun made a nightly journey from west to east.

Similar underground digging on a vast scale was carried

out by other ancient peoples—the Nubians of the Upper Nile, the Aztecs, and the Hindus. The rock-cut temple at Ipsamboul, for example, dug by Ramses II, has a depth of 150 feet, and contains colossal statues of the Pharaoh. This remarkable operation was carried out in the sixteenth century B.C.

In ancient India no fewer than one thousand underground religious structures have been identified, from Hindu temples to Buddhist monasteries, carved from the living rock, in the third century B.C. The earliest known is the Sudama Cave, cut in the twelfth year of the reign of Asoka, the Beloved of the Gods, that is, in 256 B.C.

But when we look at tunnelling in the ancient world, as in the case of so many other of the practical arts, the people who seize out attention before all others are the amazing Romans.

Hadrian's Aqueduct

In 1840, a few years after the birth of modern Greece, Athens began to expand from the decaying village which it had been under centuries of Turkish rule. The growing town needed a better water-supply system. A very surprising and gratifying discovery was made: Athens already had an excellent water-supply system, forgotten since the Middle Ages, in the form of a tunnel aqueduct built by the Romans in Hadrian's reign (second century A.D.), when the city was large. Begun about A.D. 115, Hadrian's Aqueduct was fifteen miles long, but was completed in six years by Roman engineers who sank no fewer than 700 vertical shafts 30 to 130 feet deep, providing 1,400 headings from which to drive the tunnel. Built to last, in the Roman engineering tradition, Hadrian's Aqueduct serves Athens today, having been cleaned and repaired by the American firm of Ulen and Co. in the 1920s.

Fire and Water against Rock

The Romans also did hard-rock tunnelling, and by a remarkable method. We do not know the name of the engineering genius who devised it, but the Roman way was a tremendous revolutionary advance over the Greek hammer and chisel. The Romans built a huge fire in front of the rocky face, then when the face was well heated, threw buckets of cold water, or water and vinegar, against it, causing the rock to scale or crack. A difficult and dangerous procedure, certainly, but it enabled the Romans to perform some astounding tunnelling feats.

One of the most famous, described by Pliny the Elder and by Suetonius, lies less than fifty miles east of Rome. This was the "emissary" aqueduct to carry water from Lake Fucinus (now Lake Celano) to the River Liris (now the Garigliano). Three and one half miles long, it was driven straight through Monte Salvino from shafts sunk up to four hundred feet into the intervening mountainside. Some twenty-two shafts were sunk and the final tunnel was a complicated system of inclined passages, ten feet high by six feet wide. One may easily believe Suetonius that this tunnel, completed by Claudius, required the labour of thirty thousand men for eleven years. Like many mountain tunnellers afterward, the Roman engineers encountered water inrushes, which had to be dealt with by pumping.

This tunnel was stopped up during the Middle Ages, but was reopened in the mid-nineteenth century when Prince Torlonia drained the lake.

Tunnels for the Roman Resort Traffic

Baiae, favourite resort area of Roman emperors as well as wealthy senators and knights, was cut off from Naples by the massive Ridge of Posilipo, making necessary a comfortless journey over the rocky hills. From the military point of view, too, the Posilipan Ridge was an awkward interruption between Naples and the Baiae Peninsula. In the time of Augustus (31 B.C. to A.D. 14) the engineer Cocceius drove several short tunnels in the region. Two, the Grotta di Seiano and the Grotta di Posilipo traversed the ridge. The Posilipo—called the Crypta Neapolitana by Petronius and Seneca—was frequently restored against landslides and collapses; the Seiano disappeared completely, its portals covered with earth, and was only rediscovered in 1840. Each is a little more than half a mile long. Seiano varies in bore from thirteen to twenty-one feet in width and from fourteen to twenty-eight feet in height; Posilipo is a little smaller. Seiano was apparently restricted to the Imperial service, its western portal opening on the site of the Imperial Villa Pausilypon, while the Posilipo, unprovided with shafts for sunlight, was for use of the public.

Seneca comments acidly on the passage through this dismal

gallery: "There is no prison longer than that crypta, no torch dimmer than those they shielded before us, which served not to lighten the darkness but only to look upon one another. And, in any case, even if there had been a glimmer of light, the dust would have robbed us of it; it was dense enough to be-darken an out-of-doors spot, what then is to be said of it in that place where it turns upon itself and, unstirred by any breath of wind, falls back upon those who raise it?"

Further west, beyond Lake Avernus, lies the Grotto of the Cumaean Sibyl, described by Virgil, 130 metres long and five metres (sixteen feet) high. This work was cut in the soft tufa in the fifth or sixth century B.C.; its exact origin and religious purpose remain a mystery. In excavating for this Grotto, another great Roman gallery was discovered, 180 metres long, traversing the Monte de Cuma from east to west at its base. This and another tunnel through the Monte Grillo, connecting Lake Avernus with Cumae, are part of the same military road and were apparently the work of the same Cocceius who constructed the Seiano and the Posilipo.

After the Romans

From the fall of Rome in the fifty century, man's technical progress slowed to a crawl, indeed in some fields, retrogressed In the Dark Ages no centre of economic and political power strong enough to launch important engineering enterprises existed in Europe. In the fragmented Western world the only great ventures demanding co-operation of large numbers of men that could be undertaken were marauding expeditions such as the Norman invasions of England and Sicily, the Crusades. At the same time the decline of the cities removed the principal reasons for digging tunnels—water supply and sewage disposal. Virtually the only tunnelling done in Europe during the Middle Ages was by the Moors in Spain, whose civilization was the most scientifically advanced in Europe, and who constructed water tunnels for irrigation.

During the late Middle Ages tunnelling suddenly received an important impetus from a new source—metal mining. This was carried on increasingly in Germany and other places. But the miners of the sixteenth century had made no significant advances over the Roman technique of fire and water—a painfully laborious procedure at the end of an underground shaft and gallery, since each cracking would fill the mine with smoke.

Some time around 1600 a mining engineer thought of borrowing a weapon of war and turning it into an instrument of peaceful progress. Gunpowder had been known in Europe since at least 1320, but it was nearly three hundred years before it was introduced into mining operations in Hungary and Germany. Even then its use remained strictly limited, because of the high cost of drilling in rock by hand drill and hammer.

Gunpowder Digs Canals

It was actually not until the great age of Louis XIV that Europe achieved a substantial advance over the Roman Empire in tunnelling. In the seventeenth century the multiplication of commercial enterprises and trade routes in the wealthy and well-administered kingdom of France led to an intensive expansion of canal-building. Water was then, as later, by far the cheapest form of transportation, and canals, in many parts of France, could be easily built to connect important rivers. But a canal must be absolutely level, and in many places canal engineers were faced with the alternative of either taking a wide detour around a mountain, or tunnelling through it.

By now the use of gunpowder to blast rocks in mining was well established. When Pierre de Riquet, the engineer who dug the great Languedoc Canal in 1679-81 found his path blocked by a hill of soft limestone, he determined to blast his way through it. Holes were drilled in the rock and loaded with the black gunpowder of the Royal Artillery, tamped down by wooden pegs. The detonation was followed by a shower of rock—and tunnelling with explosives was born. The Malpas Tunnel of the Languedoc Canal was 510 feet long—modest even by Roman and Greek standards—but twenty-two feet wide and twenty-seven feet high, much the biggest-bore passage ever pushed through rock.

Historically, the Malpas was of enormous importance, for it opened the way to the rapid proliferation of canals throughout Western Europe and the British Isles, breaking down the barriers to trade and industrial progress. One of the great landmarks in the history of the canal tunnel was the mile-long passage blasted by James Brindley for the Duke of Bridgewater to permit barges to pick up coal directly at the Worsley

Hill mine for shipment to Manchester. This canal was opened in 1761. Just six years later Brindley was at work on the famous Grand Trunk Canal, whose Harecastle Tunnel was a mile and a half long, nine feet wide and twelve feet high.

Tunnelling was at a stage comparable to that of a regiment whose forward units have made contact with the enemy and driven him from his outposts. But the enemy's main line of resistance still lay ahead. Before we take up the story of how that line was successfully stormed by the engineers and labourers of the nineteenth and twentieth centuries, let us look ahead at an ultimate aspect of the triumph of tunnelling. Man today has come to live mainly in cities, a very striking contrast to all former ages. Our cities, which we take so readily for granted, would simply be unliveable without the tunnel. Under our feet as we walk along the streets, far beneath us as we drive through some of our city parks, under us even as we travel by bridge or ferry over rivers and lakes, are tunnels of whose existence we are sublimely unaware, but on which we depend completely. Let us lift the cover off the modern city and see what lies underneath.

CHAPTER FOUR

The Fantastic World Beneath Your Feet

Every city dweller walks above a grotesque maze of tunnels. Under New York, for example, there are 132 miles of subway tunnels, 7,000 miles of gas mains, 5,000 miles of sewers, 2,200 miles of TV cables, 15,000,000 miles of telephone wires, 87 miles of high-pressure steam pipes, 19,000 miles of electrical cables, and 5,528 miles of water mains. Manhattan Island is no longer a rock but a honeycomb. "It's as crowded under the streets as a plate of spaghetti," was the way one New York underground worker put it. In Herald Square tracks of the B.M.T., the Sixth Avenue Independent Subway, the Hudson Tubes, the Pennsylvania Railroad, and the Long Island Rail Road converge—seventeen tracks which must pass one another at different levels. All this in addition to the gas, water, heating mains, and telephone and power cables.

The average New Yorker is only vaguely aware of such things as water and gas mains until they burst or leak and cause street disruption. Water mains burst on the average of one a day, but only create news when several come at once, as occasionally happens. Six burst mains occurred in five hours one November night in 1957, flooding the vicinity of the Metropolitan Opera House.

The electrical power that runs under New York streets is awesome. "When July heat causes every air conditioner in town to be switched on at once," says Robert Daley in *The World Beneath the City,* "manholes must be packed with dry ice and perforated garden hose thrust through the conduits in an effort to cool cables which would otherwise burn out."

Water supply has created engineering problems for every large city, ancient and modern. New York today is served principally by two huge tunnels blasted through the bedrock at stupendous depths. City Water Tunnel No. 1 passes under the Hudson at Storm King Mountain at a depth of 1,114 feet —the deepest non-mining tunnel below sea level on the face of the earth. Inside Manhattan Island it runs at 200 to 750 feet below street level. Eighteen miles long, bored from numerous shafts, it was completed in 1917. It brings a billion and a half gallons of water a day into the city. City Tunnel No. 2, necessitated by the swiftly expanding demands of the growing population, was finished in 1936. Tunnel No. 1 has a diameter of fifteen feet in Manhattan, diminishing to eleven feet in Brooklyn—it passes under the East River too. Twenty-mile-long No. 2 has a diameter of seventeen feet, and does not enter Manhattan, being built to service the Bronx, Queens, and Brooklyn. It plunges to a maximum depth of 766 feet below the surface, inside the city 553 feet below sea level. It runs farther below the surface of Manhattan than most of the skyscrapers rise above it.

Why so deep? In order to take advantage of the natural pressure built up by water descending from Catskill sources 280 feet above sea level. New York's water rushes into the city at a pressure that shoots it up into office buildings 280 feet—roughly twenty-eight stories—without pumping, an important saving.

More gas mains lie under the streets of New York today, carrying more gas into the city, than ever during the famed "gaslight era" of the mid-nineteenth century. The first gas mains, laid in lower Manhattan in the 1820s, were pipes one-half inch in diameter. They are still in place, and "modern diggers," says Daley, "puzzled, lean on their shovels and stare at them, not knowing what they are or to whom (among the many proprietors of the city's underground maze) they belong."

Among the electric light pioneers, only Edison had the foresight to string his wires through conduits under the streets of the city. All New York's power lines are underground today as a result of a bitter debate and one might almost say civil war. The rush to supply power and communications in the '70s and '80s created a fantastic forest of poles lining the city streets, ranging from fifty to ninety feet in height (occasionally even higher), carrying from two to thirty crosstrees, sustaining as many as 300 wires. The blizzard of '88 struck this bizarre festoon with devastating effect. The terrifying tangle which resulted frightened New York into action, and Mayor Hugh J. Grant, elected on a platform promising to get rid of the wires, carried out his promise by the simple expedient of sending out crews to cut down all the poles and cut up the cables. The several companies affected were forced, despite vehement resistance, to follow Edison's sensible example and take their lines underground.

Park Avenue, New York's world-famed fashionable residential street, running down the centre of Manhattan Island, is a strange reincarnation of the prehistoric Swiss lake communities; it is a world on stilts. The stilts are heavy concrete pillars sunk to bedrock, and they support the office and apartment skyscrapers while leaving room for a vast, seventy-nine-acre "basement" for midtown New York. In this basement is housed the turn-around loop for the trains of the New York Central, and the New York, New Haven & Hartford, as well as the incoming tracks running directly under the street itself.

In the great days of railways—and perhaps of Park Avenue—part of the "basement" was set aside as sidings for handcars belonging to railway officials. These apparently agile executives pumped themselves from their Park Avenue homes to Grand Central and their offices, until increased traffic made the tracks unsafe.

The great days of railways also caused the Waldorf-Astoria to be located between Park and Lexington Avenues close to Grand Central. Arriving dignitaries could have their private cars sided directly under the Waldorf, whence they were lifted to their suites.

Buildings on Park Avenue have no basements of their own. Consequently, they have a heating problem—or would have, except that the New York Steam Company, merged in 1954 with Consolidated Edison, has taken care of the problem since 1881. Today its eighty-one miles of steel steam mains, some as big as sixty feet in diameter, serve 2,400 Manhattan buildings. Most of these actually have basements, but find it cheaper to pipe in their steam.

Do subways (the normal American term for railways under the surface) ever get cleaned? This is a question many visitors ask. Of course the cars are cleaned daily, and track-walkers are continuously at work picking debris off the tracks. But what about the tunnel walls and roof? The answer is that the tunnels do get cleaned, but not very often. In fact, the first such cleaning of New York's subway tunnels is underway at this writing.

A " steam jenny" consisting of a flat-car followed by two water cars does the job. The men on the flat-car hose away accumulated dirt with a mixture of steam and detergent, the other two cars following up with a rinse. The "dirt" is mostly steel dust, ground from the friction of wheels and rails, which settles on everything, and sometimes causes short circuits.

London, Paris, Moscow, and other underground systems close part of the night, permitting more frequent cleaning without disrupting service. But in New York service is twenty-four hours a day, so except for inside stations, and in the underriver tunnels, New York subways go a long time between wash-ups.

"More than a billion gallons of water comes into New York each day—and more than a billion gallons of sewage goes out," says Daley. New York's first sewers were not built till the middle of the nineteenth century, when the Croton Aqueduct brought the first big volume of water into the rapidly growing city.

The first sewage system was an imperfect success. To correct one of its faults, the City Council ordered buckets of perfume poured down the sewers. Actually the sewage gas was more than offensive; it was highly dangerous. The sewage mains emptied directly into the rivers, and contaminated all the surrounding shores. Sewage gas also explodes from time to time. Following the example of Chicago and other cities, New York is now handling sewage by treatment plants, whose motive power is the methane gas generated by the sewage itself under treatment. Chicago, incidentally, has the world's champion long sewer tunnel—the West Side Interceptor, 20.6 miles long.

But the sewers of New York and Chicago are newcomers, practically without history, compared to the sewers of Paris, which have not only a history but a literature. What reader—or moviegoer—can forget Jean Valjean's escape from the barricade, carrying the wounded Marius? Victor Hugo, in his marvellously discursive way, was not satisfied merely to depict his hero's private adventure in the labyrinth below Paris; he chronicled in passing the whole saga of the Paris sewers in his novel *Les Misérables*.

In 1802, it seems, the sewers suddenly backed up and flooded a large area in the vicinity of the Place des Victoires. There was nothing new in this inundation; it had happened many times before. But in 1802 Napoleon was First Consul. Bruneseau, of whom Hugo gives us no anterior details, was ordered, or rather given permission, to explore the sewers. The adventure, undertaken in 1805, was a lurid sort of Odyssey. "It was not uncommon for the ladders to plunge into three feet of mire. The lanterns flickered in the miasmas. From time to time they brought out a man who had fainted. At certain places, a precipice. The soil had sunken, the pavement had crumbled, the sewer had changed into a blind well; they found no solid ground; one man suddenly disappeared; they had great difficulty recovering him. . . . They lighted, from point to point, great cages full of oakum and saturated with resin."

At certain points along his route, Bruneseau found ancient dates scratched into the stone, showing the limits of previous explorations—1550, at one of the first branchings, indicated the limit reached by Philibert Delorme, a sixteenth-century royal engineer of King Henri II. The original belt sewer dated from 1412.

Cells of ancient dungeons were discovered—dungeons apparently built into the sewers. An iron collar hung in one of the cells. Echo of Poe's tale: the skeleton of an orangutan, escaped from the Jardin des Plantes in 1800, was found. Centuries-old gold and silver coins, jewellery, precious stones, trinkets, were found too. A rag clung to the hinge of what had once been a grating; a bizarre relic of history, the rag was the shroud of Jean Paul Marat, the French Revolutionary leader stabbed to death in 1793. The bit of cloth had been "the only fine linen he had in the house," the souvenir of a love affair with a noble lady whose crest was still legible. "A marchioness had slept upon it; Marat had rotted in it; it had passed through the Pantheon to come at last to the rats of the sewer. This rag of the alcove, every fold of which Watteau would once have gladly sketched, had at last become worthy of Dante's fixed regard."

Bruneseau spent seven years in the Paris sewers, first exploring, then extending them, and, in Victor Hugo's words, "disinfecting and purifying them. Tortuous, fissured, unpaved, crackling, interrupted by quagmires, broken by fantastic elbows, rising and falling out of all rule . . . appalling, such was the ancient sewer of Paris." But thanks to Bruneseau, the sewer into which Jean Valjean stepped was, if dark and gloomy, nonetheless "neat, cold, straight, correct. It almost realizes the idea of what is understood in England by the word 'respectable'."

The figures Hugo cites are interesting. The old monarchy built barely five miles of sewers from 1412 to 1789. Napoleon and his successor, Louis XVIII, each added a mile, and Charles X (1823-30) nearly two miles. But Paris during this period grew even more rapidly than the sewers; by 1820 it was approaching a million. At the same time the nineteenth century was far less tolerant than its predecessors of the conditions resulting from a wholly inadequate sewage system. Under the July Monarchy (1830-48) over eighteen miles of sewer were constructed, to which the Second Republic added five miles in four years and the Second Empire, up to the time Hugo wrote (1862), fourteen miles more. Expansion of the Paris sewage system still continued rapidly during the generation after he wrote, often involving complex tunnelling operations under the Seine and the canals. Hugo himself mentions a problem encountered "quite recently" when a collecting sewer passing under the St. Martin Canal struck a fissure from the canal bed, which had to be located by a diver and filled with clay. Hugo further cites two directing engineers, Monnot and Duleau, both of whom died as a consequence of their arduous struggles in underground Paris. "There are no bulletins for these acts of bravery," observes the novelist, "more profitable, however, than the stupid slaughter of the battlefield."

Unexpected Discoveries under the City

Quite inadvertently, tunnellers under the great cities are often archaeologists. The world's old cities, such as Paris and Rome, have underground structures dating back centuries—sometimes, indeed, older than anything surviving on the city's surface. Quarries and mines, abandoned and forgotten, suddenly open in front of the tunnelling shield. In the extension of the Paris Métro under the Buttes Chaumont a century-old gypsum mine was uncovered, with caverns thirty feet high supported by pillars twenty feet in diameter. One level of the galleries lay 130 feet below the street surface. Whole districts of Paris and its suburbs are honeycombed with stone quarries some of which are believed to date back to Lutetia, the Gaulish city that stood on the Ile de la Cité in Caesar's time. Today these quarries represent a serious hazard against which modern

Paris must protect itself. To build her storied hotels, palaces and churches old Paris dug rock from nearby outlying districts; the quarries, once abandoned, were closed up and forgotten. Centuries later, as streets and buildings were erected above, the added weight brought the danger of cave-ins. A modern Renault truck may suddenly sink into the quarry from which the stones of the Cathedral of Notre-Dame were taken eight hundred years ago.

Most famous of the quarries of course is the Catacombs, which was first worked in Roman times. Ground subsidences in the eighteenth century, when this Montparnasse district was growing, led to security measures, after which the quarry was used to deposit bones removed from the cemeteries which the expanding city was overruning. The bones and skulls of some three million persons are said to be interred in the labyrinthine galleries.

In 1902, when the Moscow underground was first proposed, the Archaeological Society of Moscow warned that the line would pass through the sacred ground of ancient cathedrals. No one was prepared, however, for the extraordinary "secret city" built in the reign of Ivan the Terrible (1533-84), consisting of extensive caverns right under the heart of ancient Moscow, apparently constructed for defence as well as religious purposes.

In the Rome underground, too, innumerable archaeological finds were made, caves, cellars, galleries, secret underground chapels, etc., notably in the region between the Via Cavour and San Pietro in Vincolo. At another point a retaining wall which held the moat surrounding the well-known wall of Servius Tullius (sixth century B.C.) was discovered "to the annoyance of engineers and the joy of archaeologists," *The Engineer* notes.

Even in New York, subway tunnellers have made discoveries of historic interest. When the B.M.T. was under construction, the tunnellers broke into an oddly ornate little passageway under Warren Street and discovered New York's first subway, built a generation earlier by a remarkable man whose acquaintance we shall presently make.

If a Roman engineer were to inspect the works under a modern city the only thing he would understand would be the aqueducts, but these he would indeed appreciate. The Delaware Aqueduct, for example, mostly built in the 1930s to supplement New York's Catskill water supply, is 105 miles long, and entirely in tunnel, sometimes running at depths as great as 1,500 feet. It is both the longest and the deepest tunnel in the world, though these distinctions are less impressive than they seem; its depth is exceeded by numerous mine shafts and its great length, from an engineering standpoint, consists actually of some thirty short tunnels linked together.

Its construction was simply an exercise in maximum efficiency with familiar tools. Jumbo drill carriages mounting half a dozen drills bored thirty holes twelve feet deep, into which was rammed as much as 350 pounds of dynamite per attack. Huge ventilating fans, electric mucking machines and various other devices were employed; the one serious problem, crossing under Rondout Creek, was accomplished with the technique used by the Japanese at Tanna and by other tunnellers since—pumping cement grouting radially from a pilot tunnel.

The Delaware is the longest tunnel aqueduct, but it is not the longest aqueduct by a considerable distance. That distinction belongs to the Colorado River Aqueduct, a staggering combination of conduits, siphons, and canals, running a distance of 392 miles from Parker Dam on the river via Cajalco Reservoir to the city of Los Angeles and surrounding communities. This remarkable tunnel complex has been cited by the American Society of Civil Engineers as one of the "Seven Modern Wonders" of the United States. The longest tunnel is eighteen miles. The one that gave engineers the most trouble, the San Jacinto, is thirteen miles long, and at one point 14,500 gallons of water a minute poured into one heading, surely the height of irony.

Or perhaps there is irony enough in sea-coast cities like New York and Los Angeles needing to dig tunnels of enormous length to procure fresh water. If so, it is even more curious that cities on the Great Lakes are confronted with a water-supply problem. All the fresh water anybody could drink is at the doorsteps of Chicago, Milwaukee, Cleveland, and other lake metropolises, but sewage and factory-waste dumping make it unfit, at least near shore. The solution was to tunnel out under the lake far enough to be sure of pure water. Cleveland pioneered the trick back in the 1870s, and was followed by all the other Great Lakes cities. Chicago dug several such tunnels, one of them resulting in a serious disaster when a fire broke out in the "crib"—the structure built for water intake—and sixty workers suffocated. Milwaukee engineers encountered the unlikely problem of an underground river, which actually brought work to a halt for several years.

These strange under-the-lake tunnels, as well as the numerous tunnels under the rivers of such cities as New York and Detroit, were made possible by a unique engineering weapon—the tunnel shield. Among the beautifully simple and marvellously practical mechanical inventions of the nineteenth century, this remarkable tool holds a high place. Its history is fascinating; to pursue it we must return to the year 1769, the year Napoleon was born. That same year, in another part of France, another genius was born—one as famous among engineers as Napoleon is among generals.

An early French plan for the Channel Tunnel. This 1851 scheme by Hector Horeau advocated the immersed tube method. Transport would be by rail and there would be stations floating on the surface at intervals with access to the "tunnel"

During the late 1870s work actually started on the Channel Tunnel in both Britain and France. A photograph of 1880 showing the works at the Dover terminal

The Channel Tunnel project of 1876-1882. *(Left)* "Colonel Beaumont's wonderful machine, a splendid piece of Victorian ingenuity", which could have dug the tunnel in 1881 if the War Office had not stopped it. *(Right)* The pilot tunnel, built out a mile under the Channel from Dover, is still

CHAPTER FIVE

Marc Brunel Tunnels under the Thames

The boy who was born to the Brunel family of Normandy in 1769 was christened Marc Isambard, an old family name, and sent to school to become a gentleman. But though he acquired mathematics and drawing "as easily as walking," he showed no inclination whatever for Latin and Greek and to the vexation of parents and schoolmasters spent his holidays, in his cocked hat, powdered wig, and military coat, in the local carpenter's shop. An effort was made to train him for the priesthood, but his perverse interest in the mechanical arts caused his Superior to recommend another career. A retired naval officer who was a friend of the family proposed the French Navy, and arranged the necessary tutoring. After his third lesson in trigonometry the boy astonished his teacher by asking permission to make an instrument of his own design to measure the height of the spire of the Rouen Cathedral. Not long after, he was taken on board a frigate to be presented to the captain; noticing a quadrant in the captain's cabin, and not daring to touch it, he merely examined it with his eyes, returned home and in a few days produced an instrument like it. He made a second shortly after that was so accurate that he kept it all through his subsequent service at sea.

In 1786, at the age of seventeen, Marc Brunel joined his ship and sailed for the West Indies, distinguishing himself among the ship's company by his wit and his inventions, notably a musical instrument with keyboard which he contrived at Guadeloupe.

By the time Brunel returned to homeland in 1792, the French Revolution was on; shortly there followed the attempted flight of the king, the outbreak of war with the Powers, the storming of the Tuileries and the trial of Louis XVI. Young Marc, son of a conservative middle-class family, was drawn to the Royalist side, and within a few months found himself forced to flee the country. He succeeded in obtaining a passport with the help of the American vice-consul at Rouen on the pretext of going to New York to buy corn for the Navy. The American vessel was stopped and boarded by a French frigate searching for *émigrés;* to his dismay Brunel found he had lost his passport in a carriage accident just before coming aboard. Having a space of an hour or so before the search would reach him, he forged a new passport, complete with seals and stamps, so good it was passed without comment.

Arrived in America the young officer joined with two French friends in an exploring expedition to the wilderness around Lake Ontario, the object being to map, acquire, and sell tracts of land to colonists. An extraordinary coincidence enlivened the trip; canoeing up a small stream the party met another group of French *émigrés*—the Duc d'Orléans, future King Louis Philippe, and his brothers. A more significant meeting occurred on the way back to New York; the young Frenchman fell in with an American merchant named Thurman who was so impressed with Brunel's ideas about joining the Hudson to Lake Champlain by a canal that he commissioned him and his friends to make a survey. In the work that followed Brunel distinguished himself by his extraordinary ingenuity in finding ways to free riverbeds from rock, to avoid swamps, etc.

Though he had intended to stay in America only until the troubles at home were over, it was now growing evident that the troubles were of longer duration than anyone had anticipated. At the same time America was indeed a land of opportunity for a man with Brunel's talents. Back in New York he turned architect and built a whole series of buildings for the rapidly growing town on Manhattan Island, including the Park Theatre. He was appointed Chief Engineer of New York, and improved the defences and built a cannon foundry. He entered a design in the competition for a Capitol building for the new seat of government, Washington, and actually won, though for reasons of economy the judges decided to use another plan.

One evening in 1798 Brunel was dining at the home of Alexander Hamilton. A fellow *émigré* just arrived from England mentioned an English naval yard he had visited, and described the enormously complicated process of making blocks, or pulleys, for the ships. Marc Brunel threw out a suggestion for making the blocks by a simpler method, and later perfecting his idea in his own mind, resolved to take it to England. He had another reason for going to England, for when five years earlier he had fled Rouen he had left behind him a pretty English girl named Sophia Kingdom, from whom he had had English lessons, and with whom he had exchanged vows which had not been forgotten on either side during the long separation. They were married at Holborn a few months after his return and settled in Portsea, where Marc Brunel at once set about selling his block-manufacturing idea to the British Navy. So obviously valuable was his invention that he encountered relatively little of the bureaucratic opposition that might have been expected. It took several years for the proper machinery to be built and assembled and actual production begun, but by 1808 the machinery was delivering blocks at an unheard-of rate. So remarkable was the system that sightseers came to visit the yards at Portsmouth; Sir Walter Scott records a journey with his family to "the Block Manufactory." When in 1814 Czar Alexander I visited England he was so impressed that he made a standing offer to Brunel to come to St. Petersburg to work.

The Block Manufactory was no sooner running smoothly than the restless mind of Brunel turned in other directions. He invented new sawing machinery, operated by steam power, to cut up the huge oak logs which were pouring in from southern Russia for the British Navy. He invented shoemaking machinery and set up an assembly line, one of the very first anywhere, manned by convalescent soldiers, which turned out shoes at the rate of four hundred pairs a day, in nine sizes, for the British Army.

The end of the wars by no means diminished his many-channelled activity. He built a steam fire engine for the Conservatory of Arts and Crafts in Paris, and invented a double-action steam engine which was installed on the British coastal ship *Regent*. The device was extremely successful, and Brunel might have plunged deeper into the exciting prospects of steam navigation, except that the scarcity of coal in distant places made the immediate future of "windless sailing" doubtful except in coastal waters. In 1817 he produced plans for a new water supply for Paris and a great suspension bridge over the Neva at St. Petersburg. In short, Marc Isambard Brunel had become the foremost engineering talent in Europe.

But while the dawning industrial age gave brilliant opportunities to genius, it also provided financial pitfalls. Before the invention of limited liability, other inventions frequently led to debtor's prison, which was the surprising case with Brunel. His sawmills, while operating with unsurpassed mechanical efficiency, were financially mismanaged by his partners into bankruptcy, and Brunel was committed to King's Bench prison. The regimen was hardly severe; not only was Sophia allowed to move in with him, but he was permitted to leave the prison freely and walk the neighbouring streets. Nonetheless, the sentence was an unjust affront, and Brunel opened a correspondence with the Czar looking towards future employment in Russia. This stirred patriotic Englishmen to press the government, and through the efforts of the Duke of Wellington, Brunel was awarded the sum of five thousand pounds. This was actually reasonable enough, for part of Brunel's financial difficulties, at least, traced to the refusal of the government to take some eighty thousand pairs of soldiers' boots off his hands when the war suddenly ended in 1815.

At any rate, Marc Brunel agreed to remain in England. Already, before he left prison, his indefatigable genius was maturing a scheme beside which all his other ideas and inventions seemed trivial and dull. It had come to him originally when he had discussed the great bridge over the Neva with the Czar. If there were difficulties in the way of bridging a river, he asked himself if it might not be feasible, given the new steam power, to tunnel under it? True, such an enterprise would be costly, and therefore not fitting for St. Petersburg—but what about London?

Brunel was not alone in considering a tunnel under the Thames. Richard Trevithick, builder of the first steam locomotive, undertook to drive an exploratory driftway, or small-bore tunnel, under the river in 1807. If the driftway proved feasible, a regular tunnel operation would follow, using the driftway to drain off excess water. The need for such a tunnel was evident; 3,700 passengers a day were crossing the Thames by ferry in the dock area. But though Trevithick pushed his five-foot-high tunnel over a thousand feet under the river, he could not keep it from caving in—not surprising in view of his total lack of the main implements and techniques of underwater tunnelling.

One day in the Chatham Yard in 1822, Marc Brunel was sunk in thought about the Thames tunnel when he noticed a little "shipworm," the shellfish *Teredo Navalis,* boring into an oaken plank. Struck by the peculiarly effective adaptation of the animal to its task, Brunel conceived of a gigantic tunnelling instrument, unlike any machine in existence, a "shield" which could be pushed forward in a heading under a river, protecting the workmen as they excavated. Brunel's original shield design was cylindrical. The principle involved can be understood by picturing a tin can with one end removed and with a hole punched in the other end. Shove such a can forward through soft, wet sand and a trickle of sand will come through the punched hole into the can itself, whence it can be removed out the open end. But though Brunel patented a cylindrical shield on this principle, which became the archetype of later shields, the one he actually built and used under the Thames was quite different. It was rectangular in form, and made up of twelve parallel segments each of which could be moved forward individually. The reason for this was the large bore of the tunnel he wished to build—twenty-three by thirty-seven feet.

Brunel explained his shield to the Institute of Civil Engineers and subsequently to a meeting of prospective investors at the City of London Tavern. A company was promptly formed with a capitalization of £160,000, and Brunel awarded £5,000 for the use of his patent, another £5,000 when the first toll was paid, and a salary of £1,000 a year for three years—it being assumed that the tunnel would be completed in that space.

The first step was to take sample borings in the river; these proved reassuring, showing "strong blue clay, suitable for excavation," continuous across the bottom. Brunel at once resolved on a double-road tunnel, with two parallel archways, and set to work sinking a shaft at Rotherhithe on the south side of the Thames, a mile below the Tower Bridge. Here he made an all-but-fatal mistake; heeding the advice of leading geologists, he sank the shaft to a depth of only fourteen feet beneath the river bed. The truth about the tunnel route at this level was that while in the main it lay through impervious clay, it was cut by numerous seams of sand and silt, running vertically down from the river bottom, through which water could run freely. Brunel, in fact, was about to acquire through bitter pioneer experienced the first expert knowledge of subaqueous engineering.

The shield, consisting of twelve enormous, narrow cast-iron frames, fastened together and subdivided into three stories each, formed an iron honeycomb in which thirty-six men could work in individual cells. A team of bricklayers, standing on projections of the outer cells, back to back with the miners, bricked up the wall as the huge shield crept forward, powered by screw jacks braced against the end of the brick lining. A long platform followed like a tail; this was for the removal of dirt. On November 28, 1825, the shield began its forward push.

Its progress was not spectacular. The individual cells were pushed forward no more than six inches at a time, and even though two shifts were employed, early in 1836 the shield registered advances of only eight feet per week. In January water burst into the tunnel, causing a momentary panic among the workmen, but the shield held firmly, and nothing worse happened than a minor inundation.

But the rate of progress did not at all suit the directors and shareholders, and at their instance, over Brunel's better judgment, the action of the shield's frames was extended to eighteen inches per advance, and piece work introduced for the bricklayers. This did indeed speed the work, for the bricklayers, getting paid by the brick, constantly pressed the miners to push ahead. It required exceptional physical strength for a miner to advance his shield section a foot and a half, but it could be done. The hasty and irregular movements however soon carried the shield laterally off course, and Brunel had to right it by a laborious and delicate sidewise movement.

Also over Brunel's objections, the company invited visitors to inspect the tunnel at a shilling a head. This expedient produced a little revenue, but it also produced considerable apprehensions on Brunel's part. Early in 1827 the tunnel was drawing perilously close to the river bed. On April 2 a diving bell was borrowed and the river bottom examined directly above the shield. The result was hardly reassuring; with an iron rod it was found possible to probe down and strike the top of the shield. The ill-ventilated and often noxious heading had a bad effect on the men's health. In February, Brunel recorded the death of one of his engineers, and the illness of three others, including his twenty-year-old son, Isambard Kingdom Brunel. Two of the foremen were also incapacitated, and several miners, bricklayers, and muckers. On May 1, with the heading 540 feet under the river, the workmen struck and picketed the shaft. After a few days the men, who of course had no union, returned to work, except for the ringleaders, whom Brunel refused to rehire. Wages, incidentally, for these men who risked their health and their lives, ranged from three shilling three-pence to three shillings ninepence a day—considerably less than a dollar a day.

Now objects from the river bottom began turning up in front of the shield—shoe buckles, pieces of brass, etc. On May 12 a particularly ominous recovery was made—a shovel which was recognized as having been left in the river bottom in the diving-bell reconnaissance of April 2.

At two o'clock in the morning of May 18 Richard Beamish relieved Isambard Brunel as superintending engineer. The two men exchanged a few words about the hazardous state of the heading, and young Brunel, instead of going home, remained in the office at the head of the shaft. Beamish made his way to the shield where miners and bricklayers were working in apprehensive silence. Writing later, Beamish described what followed:

"At five o'clock, as the tide rose, the ground seemed as though it were alive . . . the men who came on at 6 a.m. betrayed extreme reluctance to go to work. . . .

"The tide was now rising fast. On entering the frames, Nos. 9 and 11 were about to be worked down. Already had the top polings of No. 11 been removed, when the miner Goodwin, a powerful and experienced man, called for help. For him to have required help was sufficient to indicate danger. I immediately directed an equally powerful man, Rogers, in No. 9, to go to Goodwin's assistance, but before he had time to obey the order, there poured in such an overwhelming flood of slush and water that they were both driven out. A bricklayer who also answered the call for help, was literally rolled over onto the stage behind the frames . . . I made an effort to re-enter the frames, calling upon the miners to follow; but I was only answered by a roar of water . . . I saw that the case was hopeless."

Beamish gave the order to abandon the heading. The flood

was already waist-high, most of the lights were out, cement casks and loose timber were bobbing about. The shield held, despite the volume of water pouring through Goodwin's frame, and all the men reached the shaft safely. An elderly engine man was at the last moment found to be missing, at the bottom of the shaft, but Isambard Brunel dropped down the shaft with a rope and rescued him.

The few feet of silt between the shield and the river bottom had sunk down and passed though the shield, till the river itself reached the upper section of the shield. There was now a hole in the bottom of the Thames extending down to the upper corner of the shield, and the tunnel heading was filled with water.

Brunel's solution was to load barges with clay bags and dump them into the hole. The directors had another idea, and at their insistence it was tried—a raft loaded with 150 tons of clay was sunk. It landed in a tilted position, doing no good and protecting the hole against further clay bags. With difficulty, Brunel raised it again. The diving bell was borrowed again, and both Brunels and the other engineers examined the hole. On June 27 Beamish took a boat into the heading and rowed up to where a mountain of silt had accumulated in front of the shield. Beaching his boat and scrambling over the mountain, he examined the shield and found it in good condition. A little later two directors wished to visit the shield in the same way. One incautiously stood up in the boat, bumped his head on the tunnel roof, fell and overturned the boat. A workman, drafted to man the oars, was drowned, much to the distress of Brunel.

After months of work the hole in the river bottom was plugged with clay, the heading drained, the silt shovelled and carted away and the shield ready to operate once more. On November 10, 1827, a celebration was held in the tunnel, with the band of His Majesty's Coldstream Guards playing as the engineers and directors drank toasts, in joint honour of recommencing the tunnel and the victory of the allied European fleets over the Turks in the Battle of Navarino: "Down with water and Mahomet—wine and [Admiral] Codrington forever!" In the adjoining arch a hundred miners and bricklayers echoed the toasts with beer.

The celebratory mood was short-lived. On the night of

January 12, 1828, Isambard Brunel was directing operations at the shield. The No. 1 frame, that on the extreme right, or western end of the shield, had been kept closed. At six o'clock, when the new shift came on, young Brunel decided to open the frame to hasten digging operations, trusting to the known physical prowess of two of the workmen coming on, Ball and Collins, in case it should have to be closed against an influx. But the exterior pressure was greater than he had foreseen, and the water much nearer. A solid column of ground was forced into the heading, followed immediately by an overwhelming torrent. The engineer and the two workmen strove vainly to halt it by quickly timbering the rear of the frame, but were driven off the shield stage, while at the same a rush of air extinguished the gas lights. In pitch blackness and water to their waists, they headed for the shaft, shouting warnings to the other members of the shift, many of whom had not yet arrived at the shield. The raging water tore loose the timbering around the tail of the stage, some of the pieces falling on Brunel and his companions. Brunel found himself pinned by the right leg; with a tremendous exertion he pulled himself free and staggered towards the shaft. He arrived there carried on the crest of the massive wave; saving himself, he turned and shouted for Ball and Collins. But neither these two nor four other men who had been in the shield made it to safety. Isambard Brunel himself was hospitalized for months with internal and leg injuries.

Besides the toll of six men, the tragedy was a severe financial blow to the tunnel. The public turned a deaf ear to calls for funds, which were made largely on the basis of patriotic pride. Even appeals from the Duke of Wellington, a strong backer of the tunnel, were fruitless. Marc Brunel went ahead with filling the hole in the river with 4,500 tons of clay and gravel, and draining the heading, but by August it was evident that at least for the time being fresh funds were not going to be received, and the shield was bricked into place.

Brunel, unlike many of the mechanical geniuses who created the technology of the Industrial Revolution, was not financially chained to his dream. He had plenty of resources. Yet the tunnel, through its very difficulties, had taken hold on his imagination, and he was determined to see it through. It was six years before he found a financial solution; in 1834, the Robert Peel ministry, of which the Duke of Wellington was a leading member, granted a Treasury loan of £236,000, with the stipulation, in the teeth of a good deal of injust criticism of the chief engineer, that Brunel be retained in charge.

The resumption of the work was begun by an exceedingly difficult operation, the replacement of the old shield by a new and stronger one. The extraction of the 80-ton mass from the end of the passage 400 feet under the river with the available machinery was so formidable that a director of the company asserted that he would eat any part of the shield that was removed. He had to swallow not the shield but his scepticism, for Brunel succeeded in withdrawing the old shield and replacing it with the new one, weighing 140 tons, in 9,000 parts, with no further accident than one man's bruised finger. By November 1835 the old shield was out; by March 1836 the new one in.

But the work itself proved difficult as ever; to save expenses, the Treasury, like the Company before it, refused to allow Brunel to build a drainage facility. It was a false economy. On June 21, 1836, a sudden inrush of water put a six-week stop to the work. This and subsequent inrushes had to be dealt with by hand, and the cost per foot of tunnel reached the dismaying rate of £438. Sickness among the workers again rose sharply. The working conditions were indeed appalling; the effluvia from the river bottom was so noxious—the Thames being London's principal sewage artery—that after even a small inrush the men often fell ill on the job.

In August of 1836 the centre of the river was passed. In September, despite the water, the tunnel was advanced nearly twenty feet. Heavier influxes slowed progress to barely seven feet in the month of January, 1837. In June only one foot was gained. In August 1837 the third major influx broke through the shield; engineers and workmen fled to safety. Only three months later another flooding struck, and on March 21, 1838, still another. Thus, in a space of seven months three major floodings took place; during this period the total advance made was twenty-six feet. But not a single life was lost in the torrents; any one of them, in the absence of a shield, would have trapped the whole working force. Without the shield, of course, the heading would never have got this far in the first place. Each influx was dealt with in the now-established way, by dumping sandbags of clay, and tunnelling through this clay.

The sulphurous gases, which poisoned the tunnel atmosphere,

often exploded in puffs—"fire-damp," as the miners called it —eerily lighting the gallery with its bluish flashes.

Brunel's diary for the period eloquently records the terrible difficulties of the struggle:

"Works have been very uneasy during the night . . . ground very tender . . . ground very threatening. . . . Things had a terrific appearance this morning, after a very serious struggle for the night."

And a little later:

"Illness; the men complain very much. . . . The effluvia was so offensive that some men were sick on the stage."

And in 1838:

"Heywood died this morning. Page is evidently sinking very fast. It affects the eyes—I feel much debility after having been some time below. All complain of pain in the eyes. . . . On Sunday a bricklayer fell senseless on the top floor."

Brunel himself was in the tunnel at all hours of the day and night. When at home he was awakened every two hours and given a sample of the last excavated soil. Examining it by lamplight, he sent off fresh instructions to the foreman.

On April 4, 1840, when the heading had passed beyond the low-water mark on the south shore of the Thames, the river made its last threatening gesture. Observers on the shore noticed that the bottom directly over the shield was visibly sinking. Crowds immediately collected on the neighbouring wharves, people pushed off in boats "with the vague idea," as Beamish notes, "that they might witness the destruction of the tunnel, and perhaps the struggles of those engaged in its execution." Their morbid expectations were disappointed. In the heading a noise described by the foreman on duty as "the roaring of thunder" had been followed by a rush of air, extinguishing the gas lights. Most of the men fled back through the tunnel, but a handful of battle-tested veterans, survivors of the earlier floods, stuck with the shield, alert for the first sign of water. None came.

This last river cavity was filled as usual with bags of clay, and the work again delayed, but the heading was pushed under the south shore by summer.

Up to now no shaft had been sunk on the south shore—no one had apparently had enough confidence in the tunnel to prepare it in advance. The shaft was sunk in thirteen months, and in July 1841 the shield began its final advance. Water poured in continuously—450 gallons a minute. It was as if the stubborn river, now finally conquered, still resisted to the death. Even when the shield's corner struck the brickwork of the new shaft the battle was not over. A half inch separated the major part of the shield from the shaft; through the half inch water poured every time a shutter was opened. By January 7, 1842, the connection with the south shaft was secure; but the rest of the year was required entirely to check the water influx.

Brunel suffered a stroke towards the end of 1842, doubtless the result of the tension brought on by the work. But he staged an excellent recovery, and took part in the opening ceremonies of March 25, 1843, "with a singular calmness, very unlike his former self."

Between 6 p.m. Saturday evening, March 26, and 9 p.m. Sunday, 50,000 Londoners walked through the wonderful new tunnel. Queen Victoria had already bestowed Great Britain's official accolade; in 1841 Brunel had become Sir Marc. But the bauble of knighthood was excelled by the honest popular esteem; London, Britain, the whole world were genuinely awed by Brunel's amazing feat. Within three and a half months of the opening, a million visitors from "almost all the civilized nations of the world" walked under the Thames River. The tunnel was truly the wonder of the age.

The total cost, far exceeding preliminary estimates, amounted to £468,249—nearly two and a half million contemporary American dollars.

Economically, the project was an immediate failure but a long-range fantastic success. Pedestrians at a penny a head were an insufficient economic justification, and no carriages or wagons could use the tunnel for lack of approaches, no money being forthcoming to purchase the land. The truth was, the development of the railway since the commencement of the tunnel had been so rapid that there was good reason for waiting. It was not until 1865 that the new Metropolitan Underground built the approaches and sent its trains roaring under the Thames.

The total length of the tunnel is 1,506 feet, not an extraordinary distance. But its immense bore, twenty-three feet high by thirty-seven feet wide, gave it for some eighty years the largest cross-section area of any soft-ground tunnel. It remains in regular use today, part of the Metropolitan Line of the Underground, the great surviving monument to the genius and resolution of both Brunels, father and son, who between them contributed so dramatically to the engineering feats of their century. Young Isambard Kingdom Brunel went on to become a renowned builder of bridges, railroad lines, tunnels and viaducts, and finally the creator of the revolutionary propeller-driven ocean liners.

Marc Brunel, despite his exposure to the health hazards of the Thames tunnel, lived to be eighty, amid universal honour and acclaim. But to the felicitations he received on his feat, he was in the habit of returning a succinct reply, which might be taken as the motto of his successors in the science of tunnelling: *"Si je l'avais à refaire, je le ferais mieux."* ("If I had it to do over, I'd do it better.")

CHAPTER SIX

Mont-Cenis: Tunnelling Conquers the Alps

From the dawn of history the Alpine-Jura barrier has divided Europe. One by one, the great passes were discovered by marching and migrating Celts and Romans. In 218 B.C. Hannibal led his infantry, cavalry, and elephants from Spain to Italy by way of a pass which has never been definitely identified, but which in all probability was that of Mont-Cenis, or Col de Fréjus. This pass was frequently used by Roman merchants as well as soldiers, and by their successors through the centuries. Mule-drawn wagons carried the spices of the East over it to the Champagne Fairs of the Middle Ages, and returned with Ypres cloths to be finished and dyed in Italy.

Farther to the south was a shorter pass, the Col di Tende, between Genoa and Nice, and it was here that the first attempt to tunnel through the Alps was made. The route was much less direct than one of the more northern passes, but the tunnelling distance would be only two miles. Yet a two-mile tunnel sufficient for horse-drawn carriages and wagons was a stupendous undertaking in the fifteenth century. The advantage, of course, would be a year-round route to France and the Low Countries. At any rate, the enterprising and avaricious merchants of Genoa and the other cities wanted the tunnel, and for years work was carried on by the old, painfully laborious firing-and-cooling method. Perhaps it would have been completed, except that in 1494 Vasco da Gama reached the East by way of the African cape, and at a stroke snatched the fabulous spice trade from the hands of the Italians and placed it in those of the Portuguese. The Col di Tende tunnel was abandoned and forgotten for three hundred years, until new economic forces in the awakening eighteenth century caused the King of Piedmont-Sardinia to reopen the heading and push the work for several years; then the outbreak of the wars of the French Revolution stopped it again. Napoleon put an end to this tunnel scheme for a long time by building a practicable carriage road over the pass.

But the nineteenth century soon brought enormous new trade pressures on the Alpine barricade, and when the steam railway made its presence felt, tunnelling the Alps became an imperative. A steam locomotive could pull a thousand times the load a mule team could handle—but only provided the grades were very moderate—less than three per cent. The revived north Italian cities found themselves cut from a promising commerce with France, the Low Countries, Switzerland, and Germany. Piedmont-Sardinia, the economically prosperous and politically active little kingdom which occupied the north-west corner of Italy, could not even push its new railway lines to its own frontiers because of the intervention of the Cottian Alps between Piedmont and Savoy, the French-speaking western province. At the same time, the political orientation of Piedmont towards France, the country to which it looked for aid in its struggle against Austria, made a rail connection in this direction strategically desirable.

It was in 1838 that a contractor named Joseph Médail, who lived in Bardonnèche, on the western slope of the Col de Fréjus at Mont-Cenis, first suggested that a tunnel could be driven under the pass. The Piedmontese government listened with a mixture of sympathy and scepticism. Tunnels were being constructed in the Appenines for the new railways, but nothing remotely like the length—at least seven miles—demanded here. Henri Maus, the Belgian chief engineer of the Piedmontese railway, became interested. Professor Angelo de Sismonda, a distinguished geologist of the University of Turin, was consulted, and gave his opinion that a tunnel through Mont-Cenis was a practicable project. The optimism of Maus and Sismonda was, however, restrained; they thought the tunnel could be driven in a matter of thirty-five to forty years.

The problems of a long-distance tunnel through rock were indeed formidable. The most important were three:

1. *Heat*. As all geologists knew, temperature increases with depth at a rate usually of one degree Centigrade for every forty to sixty metres of depth. Since the maximum depth of a tunnel under Mont-Cenis would be about 1,600 metres, the rock temperature of the heading might very well reach the neighbourhood of 55° C., or 100° F. Blasting would raise this

by another 20° F., making it seriously doubtful if men could live and work.

2. *Air.* Black powder produced a thick, greasy, opaque smoke which even in the open air of the battlefield hung in dense clouds, causing men and horses to choke and gasp, and blackening faces and uniforms. Inside a deep tunnel heading, how could this almost solid smoke be cleared enough to permit work?

3. *Drilling.* Punching a hole in solid rock was a trick which in the middle of the nineteenth century was still done by the painfully laborious method of hundreds of years earlier, the two-man hand drill. If the blasting holes had to be drilled at Mont-Cenis by this method, forty years seemed a rashly sanguine estimate of the time needed.

But in the middle of the century the air was full of projects and proposals for solving the triple problem of mountain tunnelling. Maus conceived the idea of cutting through the rock by drilling alone, thus reducing the heat problem and solving the air problem. If a machine could be built to pepper the face with enough holes in a short enough space of time, a collapse might be brought about by blows of sledge hammers. Maus built a machine, a ponderous giant armed with five rows of drills, its power to be derived from the swift falling Alpine streams, transmitted to the working face by cables and pulleys. It was ingenious, but it did not work. This dream, in fact, of a machine capable of boring through rock without the aid of explosives, is one which only today is becoming a reality, as we shall see in a subsequent chapter.

But if a machine could not be made to cut enough holes to eliminate blasting, it was quite conceivable that one could be made to cut orthodox drill holes at a rate much more rapid than that achieved by hand. And in fact an English engineer named Thomas Bartlett, who had been given the contract for a section of the new Victor Emmanuel Railway had designed an efficient steam drill to make bore holes for his tunnels. In ten minutes the Bartlett drill could produce a hole thirty-three centimetres (a little more than a foot) in depth. Unfortunately, the Bartlett could not be used in such a tunnel as the Mont-Cenis, because steam power could not be transmitted over long distances without significant loss. And, of course, there still remained the problems of heat and air.

A stroke of genius was required, and the stroke came from nearby Geneva. One of the most brilliant scientific men of the time was Professor Daniel Colladon, of the famed University of Geneva. For years Colladon had been experimenting with compressed air, and had long considered its possibilities in tunnel-building. He had even suggested its use to Marc Brunel as a means of keeping water out of the facing under the Thames. Professor Colladon of course knew all about the Mont-Cenis project and its difficulties; he approached the Piedmontese government through a friend in the ministry, and was given assurances of substantial rewards and patent security. Setting to work at once, he produced at the end of two years' time a system of devices for transmitting compressed air from a source outside a tunnel without loss of compression. The air could perform multiple functions: it could control the temperature, it could ventilate, it could clear out drill holes, it could supply the power for drilling.

Now everything was ready except for the drill itself. By a fortuitous coincidence, a trio of engineers at the University of Turin were at work on a compressed air "ram," designed to operate a stationary device supplying extra power to locomotives on steep grades. The chief of the trio was Germain Sommeiller, an associate of both Maus and Bartlett on the Victor Emmanual Railway, and himself a native of the Savoyard slopes of the Alps. It occurred to Sommeiller that his ram could be made to operate a drill, a drill with more power than Bartlett's and with the inestimable advantage, for the Mont-Cenis tunnel, of deriving its motive power from compressed air.

The Piedmontese Parliament enthusiastically approved the use of the Sommeiller and Colladon machinery and ordered work commenced on the tunnel. Sommeiller was made engineer in charge.

This was in 1857. The new machines, whose hydraulic compressors were to be manufactured in Belgium, would not be ready for some time, but work was begun at once from both headings by the old-fashioned hand method. The results afford a striking comparison. In thirty-eight months only 725 metres of tunnel were bored at both ends, a rate which would have brought completion somewhere around 1910.

But in January 1861 the first Sommeiller drill made its

appearance in the south heading. With its mount it was eleven feet long, and weighed seven hundred pounds. The business end was a set of steel bits to which were imparted three motions —reciprocating (back and forth), rotating and feed (pressure forward). Not surprisingly, the machines broke down very frequently at first, and progress at the end of a year was actually slower than by hand. But Sommeiller stuck to his drill, and slowly improved both its maintenance and the efficiency of his crews. The heading moved at an accelerating pace; by 1863 progress was well over a metre a day, three times as rapid as by hand-drilling. The machinery was installed in the north heading too, and from this point on the completion of the tunnel within a few years was assured.

This is hardly to say that the work went easily. Tunnelling was carried on in a cycle of four major steps:

1. Drilling
2. Firing
3. Ventilating
4. Mucking

The first step consisted of pushing the drill up to the rock face and boring about eighty holes in a series of concentric circles. This process took no less than twelve hours.

For the second step, the sappers came forward, stuffed the holes with long cartridges of black powder and plugged them with wooden plugs. Through each plug a fuse was drawn and touched off. For step three, Professor Colladon's ventilating equipment was turned on to cool and clear the blast area. Then the muckers came forward, shovelled the rock debris into their horse-drawn wagons, and hauled it out of the heading.

All of this activity was carried on only in the restricted limits of the advance heading. This was a small gallery, about seven feet in diameter, placed at the bottom of the full tunnel bore and driven several hundred yards ahead of the finishing crew. The tunnel was enlarged to full diameter by labourers armed with hand drills, picks and shovels—with some use of machine drills.

Since the full cross section of the tunnel was seven and a half metres by six (twenty-four feet by nineteen and a half), the bulk of the excavating, it will be seen, was done by the hand labour of the following crew. This hand labour was ingeniously organized. First, from the advance heading short shafts were hewed upward to the top of the future tunnel diameter. Then these short shafts were connected to form a top heading, separated from the bottom heading by a layer of rock, broken by the shaft holes.

Now, while one crew was pushing this top heading a few hundred yards behind the blasts of the advance heading, a third crew, farther back, worked to widen the shoulders of the top heading. The drawings below show the cross section of the tunnel in the early stages of construction.

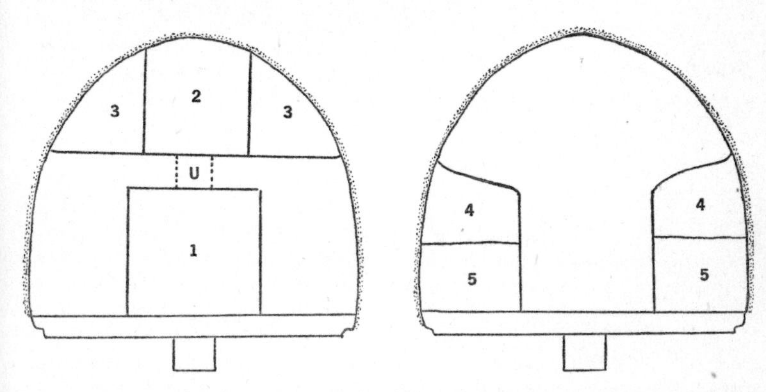

MONT-CENIS: Cross-section of two stages. *Left*, order of advance, bottom and top headings. *Right*, order of final stage. U-upraise.

The advantage of placing the advance heading at the bottom can be seen; the following crews could simply shovel the debris through the upraises and chutes—other vertical shafts—onto the wagons below.

Eventually, of course, as the tunnel pushed deeper under the mountain, still more crews went to work on the middle layer and the lower shoulders.

The advance heading was only seven feet by seven—just large enough to provide working room for the men and animals. The drill holes were positioned for maximum efficiency and detonated in series as shown in the diagram overleaf.

The *élite* of the labour force was the attacking crew, composed of about sixty-five men. Half were engaged in moving and operating the huge drills. Six sappers followed to plan and fire the charges; after the blasting, twenty muckers took over to clear away the debris. The horse-drawn wagons ran on temporary rails for easier traction.

The following crew, hundreds of men, naked to the waist, was strung out for a quarter of a mile or more behind the advance, chipping away on their various levels and galleries with hammers and drills.

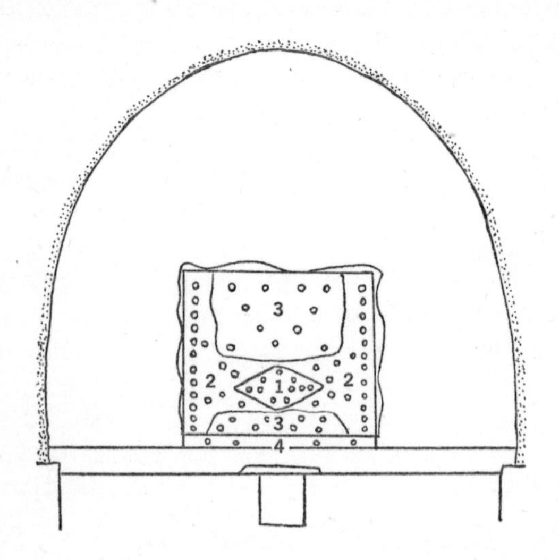

MONT-CENIS: Pattern of attack, showing drill holes and order of blasting for advance heading.

Note that the core (1) has the most drill holes; once the core and the sides (2) were detonated, the big No. 3 section collapsed fairly easily. No. 4, bottom, was blasted as a wholly secondary operation.

The scene inside the heading was murkily fantastic. The walls dripped continuously. The oil lamps hardly penetrated the black smoke which virtually filled the entire heading, from face to portal. The jets from Professor Colladon's compressed-air hoses cleared only the area directly in front of the face, to permit the attack crew to operate. From there on back the smoke simply hung in the tunnel. The labourers, breathed it, half-choked from it, often were overcome by it. It was impossible to see more than a few feet. One English visitor reported, "I could not see a lamp on the opposite side. The horses and wagons passed, but I could not see them. This continued up to within one hundred yards of the end, when a light could be seen for twenty yards . . . I was in about an hour, and when I came out I spit as black as though I had dined on lampblack."

This British observer, an experienced engineer, doubted that the tunnel could be finished under such conditions. He was probably mistaken, but actually the conditions altered considerably a year after his visit, which took place in 1866. The change was due to the remarkable new invention of a Swedish chemist named Alfred Nobel.

In 1863 Nobel had demonstrated the effectiveness of nitroglycerine as a blasting agent. By 1867 he had his high explosive conveniently packaged in the form of dynamite. Sommeiller promptly seized on the new tunnelling weapon; dynamite instead of black powder was stuffed into the Mont-Cenis drill holes. The great advantage was that fewer drill holes were needed, accelerating the progress of the advance heading, and since this was the slowest part of the work, of the whole tunnel. It also made the atmosphere inside the tunnel considerably less eerie and poisonous. One of the characteristics of Nobel's new invention was that it produced so little smoke that in its military form it became known as "smokeless powder." The scene inside the heading was no longer the choking gloom of 1866; though hardly as bright as daylight, one could see, at least, by the smoking kerosene lamps. Of course the walls still dripped, and occasionally even spurted, and the air remained inadequate. But the tunnel was livable.

The scene outside was like the rear echelon of an army in combat. Long wooden sheds housed huge drill-repair shops, for the Sommeiller drill, in that day of soft steel, used up bits by the thousand. Often a bit did not last for a single complete drilling. Other long sheds were barracks for the men. A corral for horses stood outside the portal. Wagon-repair shops, stores, hospitals, kitchens, forage depots, gunpowder depots, and other temporary buildings were crowded into the mountainside base. Prominent curiosities for the tourists who came to visit were the great hydraulic compressors. But visitors to these mountain headings were not nearly so numerous as the crowds whose safety had often given concern to Brunel under the Thames.

The hardest drilling and slowest progress came at two points where a mass of quartzite was encountered. Through this very hard rock the drill holes were pushed only a third as deep as normally—about one foot. Into the shallower holes the usual dynamite charges were rammed. Thus three attacks were necessary to gain a metre through this unyielding material, whereas through the usual gneiss or schist each attack gained nearly a metre. Luckily, the quartzite seam extended only eighty metres in one instance, one hundred in the other.

Seven thousand metres from the southern portal the workers encountered a warm spring, water flowing into the tunnel at a temperature of 85° F. The incident did not seriously disrupt work; it was, in fact, a very mild foretaste of a type of difficulty future Alpine tunnellers would encounter.

Rock temperatures, too, remained moderate, the highest recorded, under the summit, being 86° F.—an uncomfortable working temperature in the relatively high humidity, but not an impossible one.

Early in the progress of the work, a tremendous political event had taken place, profoundly altering the whole Italian peninsula and even transforming the Mont-Cenis tunnel itself. The Austrian Empire having fallen into the cleverly laid trap of Count Cavour, war had broken out in the spring of 1859. The *casus belli* had arisen for France under the terms of the secret treaty between Cavour and Napoleon III, a French army had poured into Piedmont and in two great bloody battles, Magenta and Solferino, had battered open the door to a free and united Italy. The following year, the picturesque patriot Garibaldi led his thousand Red Shirts in a fantastic filibustering expedition that overran the island of Sicily, recrossed to the mainland and overthrew the decaying Kingdom of Naples. The whole peninsula, save Venetia and Rome, became an enormously enlarged Piedmont—the Kingdom of Italy.

As a result of Piedmont's acquisitions the clause of the French-Piedmontese treaty relating to French territorial compensation came into effect, and France annexed the two French-speaking Italian districts west of the Alps—Nice, birthplace of Guiseppe Garibaldi, and Savoy, homeland of Germain Sommeiller. The Mont-Cenis tunnel was rendered international; the north portal now stood on French soil. A new financial arrangement was worked out whereby France eventually contributed 27,000,000 francs of the total cost of 75,000,000.

In the winter of 1870 the two headings drew together, and on Christmas Day the last blast holed through. The total length of tunnel bored was 13,444 metres—over eight miles.

A feature of the tunnel design to which little attention had been paid at the time was the cause of a tragedy after the completion. In June of 1871 the first three trains were sent through. All three of the engineers were overcome by smoke; two died of asphyxiation.

The source of the disaster lay in the grade of the tunnel—a sharp 2.5 per cent. Locomotives ascending from the north portal were surrounded by their own smoke. Consternation gave way to determination, and some of the new "smoke-consuming" engines—developed for the new London Underground Railway—were imported from England. Experimental trips with these new engines proved successful, and the great tunnel was formally opened on Sunday, September 17, 1871.

In this moment of triumph for the Italian national liberation movement—Rome had been annexed as the capital scarcely a year before—the ceremonies inaugurating service through the Mont-Cenis naturally stressed the Italian national aspect of the achievement. But one of the striking things about the Mont-Cenis Tunnel was its internationalism. It owed its existence to two railway engineers, one Belgian, the other British; to a Swiss professor of physics, to an engineer whose very nationality changed during the course of the tunnelling, and finally, to a Swedish chemist.

Alfred Nobel's invention had actually been used for tunnel-blasting in another place a year before Sommeiller introduced it at Mont-Cenis. This other tunnel, full of fascination for several reasons, was actually begun before Mont-Cenis, but took much longer to complete. To visit it we must cross the Atlantic to Massachusetts, where the first major American tunnelling exploit was undertaken.

CHAPTER SEVEN

Massachusetts and "The Great Bore"

The honour of the very first American tunnelling operations goes to Pennsylvania, where two small canal tunnels were dug in the 1820s. In the history of world tunnelling however, these merit only very passing mention. Of real interest is an ambitious project entertained by Boston merchants at about the same time, and eventually carried out—though with excruciating procrastination.

The Erie Canal gave New York its paramount position as port city for the booming West, and the Boston men conceived a canal of their own to equalize the advantage. The difficulty was, such a canal would have to pass through the Green Mountains, specifically, following the natural canal route, Mount Hoosac, a 1,700-foot elevation west of North Adams, Massachusetts. The tunnel would have to be from four to five miles in length, and in 1830 it is hardly surprising that its promoters were regarded as a wild-eyed set of visionaries. Neither dynamite nor compressed-air drilling had yet been dreamed of.

All the same, the attempt was not delayed by lack of confidence. America's entrepreneurs and engineers were as mettlesome as Europe's, and ready to tackle anything if it promised a profit. But a new intruder on the transport scene gave the promoters pause. This was of course the railroad. A rail line west from Boston would also need a tunnel through Hoosac, but a rail line could be, and in fact was, built farther south to connect Boston with the other railroads running west. This line, the Western Railroad, completed in 1842, at once became the implacable enemy of the Hoosac tunnel. Nonetheless, a group of backers organized the Troy and Greenfield Railroad Co., with the aim of constructing a line from Greenfield, Massachusetts, to the Vermont Line, there to connect with a line from Troy, New York. In 1848 this group successfully petitioned the State Legislature, over the protests of the Western Railroad, for permission to build their road.

Three years later the Troy and Greenfield people were back at the State House. Their plan to tunnel through Hoosac had stirred an extremely moderate response from the investing public, and they now sought the credit of the State of Massachusetts in the amount of $2,000,000 to get on with their project. This was no trifling sum in 1851; the Legislature turned down the request for $2,000,000.

Possibly had the promoters foreseen the long and painful struggle they were about to embark on they would have quit in advance. Instead they looked around for a cheap and easy way to do the tunnelling job. Someone sold them a bill of goods in the form of a monster machine, said to weigh seventy tons, which was supposed to operate like a giant cooky cutter. It mounted multiple drills (steam-operated) which were designed to cut a groove around the circumference of the tunnel heading, leaving the core to be blasted by gunpowder. The monster succeeded after several months in making a total advance of ten feet into the mountain. Perhaps this was just as well, since there would have been no way to transport steam power to it once it got deeper.

Back to the Legislature came the Troy and Greenfield Railroad, hat in hand, and this time, despite the vociferous remonstrances of the Western Railroad, the Troy and Greenfield got its $2,000,000 in state-backed credit.

Armed with this sum, the jubilant promoters sought a new contractor and a new engineer. The new engineer was an exceptional man, a West Pointer named Colonel Herman Haupt who, like George B. McClellan and others, had quit the peacetime army for a railroad career. A brilliant mathematician and another of a treatise on bridge-building, he was chief engineer of the Pennsylvania Railroad. Called in at first as a consultant on the Hoosac, he wrote a favourable report and joined in the effort to raise private capital for the tunnel.

Colonel Haupt found himself confronted with the problem of constructing a tunnel four and three-quarter miles long, with a bore twenty to twenty-two feet high by twenty-four feet wide, if the tunnel was to be double-track.

He at once recommended reducing the bore to a single-track fourteen by eighteen feet. Next, he set to work on the problem of a drill. The idea of compressed air as a source of power for tunnel drills had now been publicized, though no such drill had been put into practical form. The machine which Haupt designed consisted of a cylinder whose piston was worked by compressed air, with a mechanism for rotation and feed. It worked—but not well enough. It broke down frequently; progress was slow. When the east heading, the only one which the drill was used, had been pushed 4,250 feet, barely a sixth of the total distance, funds gave out.

Haupt was not discouraged; he urged his partners—he was a director in the Troy and Greenfield—to try to raise more capital and to apply to the state again; he himself spent his own money in efforts to improve his drill.

At this moment came the news of Fort Sumter. The government in Washington, striving to mobilize armies, found itself with a bewildering transportation tangle on its hands. A whole collection of big and little railroad lines, all needed by the Army, were all operating under separate private management. A railroad czar was needed—the country's first—and Herman Haupt was called in. Despite the unfinished business in Massachusetts, into which he had sunk all his funds, he accepted the call. His success in putting the railroads effectively to work for the Union brought him lasting fame, though it did not help him get his money back from the Hoosac tunnel.

The State of Massachusetts found itself in a quandary. The adversaries of the tunnel pointed out that the state had already sunk $2,000,000 in credit to a bankrupt company. The tunnel's supporters insisted that the only way to recover value for the money spent was by completing the tunnel. From then on the engineering history of the Hoosac tunnel is all but overwhelmed by its polemical history, for the rival railroad lines fought like tigers. Strong suspicions of bribery developed as various members of the Legislature became identified as pro- or anti-tunnel. Newspapers naturally took sides with violence: the Boston *Bee,* Boston *Advertiser* and other papers for, the Springfield *Republican*—down in the Western Railroad's part of the state—dead set against. Pamphlets poured from the presses. Speeches, letters to the editor, broadsides, memorials, and "remarks" were reprinted.

Some of these are quite edifying and illustrative of an aspect of the spirit of the age. Here are samples of what became known as the controversy over "The Great Bore."

THE MODERN MINOTAUR

Once a year a ship, laden with the richest jewels of her people, left the port of ancient Athens. The time for the annual tribute to the Minotaur had come. Athens's noblest citizens, in sad procession, attended the victims to the Piraeus, imploring for these young men and maidens, the bravest and most beautiful of her youth, the benedictions of the Commonwealth. . . .

Once a year a demand is made for the treasures of her citizens upon our modern Athens. The time of our annual contribution to a relentless destroyer has come. True, our sons and daughters are not literally required for the sacrifice; but the products of our industry, the hard-earned fruits of muscle and brain, are born to those dismal caverns of the Hoosac Mountain, from which there are no outward steps. . . .

DEATH OF OUR MINOTAUR

(Reply to the above)

The gory locks of the Hoosac Tunnel have given Frank Bird, the Walpole dyspeptic, another turn, and he pours out fifty-three pages of Pecksniffian lamentations and abuse, drawn from the never-failing fountain of spleen and remorse which constantly engulphs (sic) his guilty mind. . . .

. . . With the malice of a fiend, he haunted the State House from the coal hole to the dome, prostituting every faculty to the accomplishment of his scheme, which was the ruin of Haupt and Co., and stopping the work on the road and tunnel.

THE LOBBY

(From the Springfield *Republican*)

The chief man of them all is E. D. Foster, of Cheshire, a rough, tobacco-chewing Yankee, who was cut out for a first-rate horse jockey, but is probably spoiled now for any honest (?) occupation. . . . The lobby assignation house is at No. 5, Avon Place, a quiet if not respectable locality. . . . The proprietor is Charles Hayward, formerly a lawyer of Springfield, or perhaps it would be more correct to say, the proprietor is Mrs. Hayward, his wife. . . . There the members of the Legislature are invited to a "free and easy" every Tuesday and Thursday evening during the session. . . . For this lobby, with its corrupting influences, Massachusetts is indebted to the Hoosac Tunnel. . . .

(Adapted from Oliver Wendel Holmes):

When "lobbyists" no longer steal,
And pay for what they stole before;
When the first locomotive's wheel
Rolls through the Hoosac Tunnel's bore;

Till then let Cummings blaze away,
And Miller's "friends" blow up the globe;
But when you see that blessed day
Then order your ascension robe!

(An open letter addressed to Herman Haupt)

H. Haupt, Esq.:

. . . Do not flatter yourself that "a more intimate acquaintance will make us friends." I once had a certain estimate of your character . . . I have now a well-settled opinion. . . .

Your whole capital now consists in whining appeals for sympathy. . . . You have lost no property in this enterprise; 1st because you were not worth a dollar when you commenced it . . . in truth, you were bankrupt when you came here. . . .

. . . Don't thrust yourself among honest men. Stand in the dock where such as you belong. . . . You have attempted and well-nigh accomplished the introduction into Massachusetts of the tactics which have degraded and demoralized New York and Pennsylvania politics and legislation; what have you to say why sentence should not be pronounced?

Mr. Clerk, enter the verdict:

banished from Massachusetts

(signed) F. W. Bird

Herman Haupt was actually guilty of doubtful judgment in recommending the attack on Hoosac without having a tested drill in hand; yet his recklessness was certainly no greater than that of Brunel or Sommeiller or any of several other great tunnellers we encounter. His sincerity and honesty are beyond doubt, as is his engineering talent.

What finally happened to the tunnel? The Legislature voted to attempt its completion directly, and work was recommenced in 1864. To speed it, a central shaft was sunk; due to the peculiar configuration of the mountain it was only 775 feet in length. A short (300-foot) shaft was also sunk near the western portal to help the work there. But from the point of view of tunnelling history, the most notable event in the whole operation was a change in technique which gave the Hoosac a notable first in tunnel construction.

This was the introduction of nitro-glycerine. Thomas Doane, chief engineer for the state, had heard of Alfred Nobel's new explosive and learned in 1866 that an American had been appointed agent for it. He promptly invited the agent, T. P. Shaffner of New York, to come to Massachusetts and demonstrate. Shaffner brought his samples up to North Adams, and setting charges in drill holes made in rock outside the tunnel mouth, produced highly gratifying detonations. Doane immediately arranged for a contract with the Nobel firm, under which a nitro-glycerine factory, the first in America, was built at North Adams.

There were a few details about the use of nitro-glycerine that were not yet well known. The charges were set off by electrical fuses. One day a workman walking through the tunnel in rubber boots accumulated a charge of static electricity The naked end of the short bit of wire leading to the charge lay on the tunnel floor; when the man picked it up to attach it to the fuse he blew himself up. On the whole, accidents were surprisingly few.

But even with better drills and nitro-glycerine, progress was mediocre. The central shaft sank at a painfully sluggish rate. In 1868 it had descended only six hundred feet. Amid a fresh storm of vituperation in press and pamphlets, the Legislature decided to turn the tunnel once more over to a private contractor. Part of the reason may have been the rumours of graft with which the State House atmosphere was thickened during the period of state operation of the tunnel. By this time a total of $7,000,000 had been spent on "The Great Bore," which was no more than a quarter completed. A group of legislators sounded out Herman Haupt—now a general, and garlanded with the laurels of war—about resuming the job. The general, no doubt sensible of the personal abuse to which he had been subjected in his adventure in Massachusetts, gave a somewhat lofty reply, criticizing several steps that had been taken since the severance of his own connection with the tunnel. He considered the central shaft—which had still not reached the tunnel axis—a great waste of time, and added that it would not improve, but inhibit ventilation. He also thought it a mistake to have made the tunnel double-track; a single-track tunnel would be adequate to the railroad's needs for some time to come, and could always be converted to twin-tube if necessary later on. He estimated the cost of completing the tunnel at $5,500,000.

In view of the violence of the renewed controversy, it is doubtful if General Haupt would in any case have been invited back to Massachusetts, but the Legislature actually succeeded in getting a cheaper price than his estimate. W. and J. Shanley of Montreal agreed to complete the tunnel for $4,594,268. The Shanley firm set no tunnelling records, but it made steady progress, eventually achieving a rate of about 350 feet a month from both headings, nearly equal to the Mont-Cenis average rate. The tunnel was finally holed through on November 27, 1873. Enlarging and lining took another year, and the first train, loaded with legislators and dignitaries, passed triumphantly through in February 1875.

The "Great Bore" had taken twenty-four years to build, and what it had cost was not very clear, since apparently no two accountants could agree on a figure. Some years later, in connection with the interest payments on the bonds, a total of $14,000,000 was mentioned. The Mont-Cenis, almost twice as long, was completed in fourteen years at a cost of only $15,000,000.

As an engineering feat, the Hoosac tunnel occupies a modest place. Yet, apart from its noteworthy innovations of nitroglycerine and electrically fired charges, the Hoosac is a history-making enterprise. Despite all its difficulties, technical, financial, and political, even the relatively undistinguished progress of the Shanley stage proved to America that rock-tunnelling was a fully practical proposition. In a country whose great railroad lines would necessarily have to traverse major mountain ranges, this fact was of no small significance. Furthermore, though the Hoosac was overshadowed by its mighty Alpine contemporary, its length was not trifling—it remained the longest tunnel in the United States until the Moffat tunnel was driven through the Rockies in the 1920s.

As for Herman Haupt, the undeserving target of so much abuse, he recovered a slight part of his financial losses on the Hoosac when, in 1884, Massachusetts, wishing to clear its title to the tunnel, settled its obligations to the original contractors by paying off eight cents on the dollar. General Haupt at the time was busy directing the construction of the Northern Pacific Railroad. Sixty years earlier, when the Hoosac tunnel was first proposed, Boston businessmen had dreamed of a connection with western New York State!

CHAPTER EIGHT

Alfred Beach: American Genius at Work

When was New York's first subway built? The average well-informed New Yorker is apt to guess about 1900, which is indeed the date of the commencement of the vast subway network which proliferates under the city today. But the right answer to the question is 1868. The subway was a short one—just a block long, in fact—but it was a true subway and for several reasons a very notable one. For one thing, it remains the only tunnel in history dug by a magazine editor.

Alfred Ely Beach, a frail, scholarly man, neatly clean-shaven in an era of luxurious beards, possessed the courage and determination that characterize the professional type more often than the general public supposes. His father, Moses Yale Beach, belonged to the generation of inventive New England Yankees who made Springfield and other Massachusetts towns famous. While Alfred Beach was getting his schooling at the Academy at Monson, Massachusetts, his father turned from inventing to publishing, buying the New York *Sun* from his brother-in-law, Benjamin H. Day. When Alfred graduated, he headed for New York and the *Sun*. At twenty-two he became co-publisher with his brother Moses Sperry, but already, two years before, he had bought the just-launched *Scientific American*, and he soon found that here was where his real interest lay. Abandoning the prosperous *Sun* to his brother, he concentrated on the magazine, into whose operation he introduced a remarkable new feature: in the very first issue appearing under his aegis he announced that patents could be secured through the Scientific American Patent Agency. Over the next several decades, thousands of inventors' patents were personally serviced by Beach, who visited Washington punctually every two weeks. It was a unique and valuable stimulus to American invention, but Beach very soon showed that he was no mere patent lawyer. In 1847, when he was twenty-one, he applied for his own first patent—for a typewriter. A few years later, in

1853, at the Crystal Palace Exhibition, New York's first world's fair, he exhibited a fascinating and ingenious form of this machine—a typewriter designed to produce embossed lettering for the use of the blind. The technical triumph of making male and female dies meet with precision was much remarked on by engineers, and the general arrangement of the machine represented a permanent advance towards the modern typewriter.

Beach got into the tunnelling business through a combination of two inspirations which came to him in the next few years. One was the pneumatic tube, which he conceived as a method of delivering mail inside a city. The other was a cable-drawn street-railway system, with stationery engines, which he patented in 1864. Dissatisfied with the cable railway, and much taken with the pneumatic tube, whose efficacy he demonstrated by experiment, he asked himself why the tube idea should not be applicable to the city transportation problem. What would be needed would be simply a very powerful fan to push the air into the tube, or, reversed, pull it out. At the Fair of the American Institute, held in the Fourteenth Street Armory in 1867, he exhibited a tube, 107 feet long, suspended from the armory ceiling, in which a car was driven back and forth by a ten-foot fan turning at 200 revolutions per minute. The car carried ten passengers, and during the course of the fair made thousands of trips. The tube was constructed of laminated wood, and the car fitted loosely, with an inch or so of windage, to minimize friction.

Beach resolved to prove the practicability of his pneumatic tube as a metropolitan underground railway. A serious obstacle stood in his way—the notorious Boss Tweed, who controlled the city and much of the state government and who derived a lucrative graft from the existing streetcar companies. Beach decided that the best way to circumvent Tweed's anticipated opposition to a subway was by secrecy. Instead of asking the legislature for a charter to build a subway, he asked only for a charter for a four-foot diameter pneumatic tube, to demonstrate mail delivery by the new method. The charter was granted, and Beach promptly set to work to dig his subway.

Lower Broadway between Warren and Murray Streets was selected as the site for the experiment. The tunnel would be about 300 feet long, with a bore of about eight feet. Since the whole project had to be kept secret, Beach could not disturb street traffic with a trench cut, and consequently had to drive a real—though short—tunnel. His unhesitating solution to the problem—designing and building a cylindrical tunnel shield—is truly astonishing. No such mechanism existed anywhere. Two patents had been taken out for a cylindrical shield, both in England, one by Brunel in 1822, and one by Peter William Barlow in 1864. Possibly Beach knew of Barlow's patent, but there are reasons for doubting it; it actually seems more likely that he knew of neither Barlow's nor Brunel's cylindrical design, but only of the huge rectangular shield Brunel had actually used under the Thames. This shield was famous; Brunel's earlier design, and Barlow's patent of 1864, were obscure. And given Brunel's basic idea—an iron curtain with a window, that could be forced forward—it is not surprising that a highly intelligent man a generation later, when confronted with the problem of driving small-bore tunnels, should hit on a one-piece cylindrical shape. But what an inconceivable irony, that the archetype of one of engineering's most important tools was created to outwit Boss Tweed!

Beach introduced a new refinement. Where Greathead followed Brunel in using manual screw jacks to advance his shield, Beach used hydraulic rams, powered by hand pumps. The curved entrance to the tunnel was built of cast-iron segments, the rest simply lined with brick and cement. There was of course no need to use compressed air. The job took fifty-eight days, or rather nights, for under the supervision of Beach's twenty-one-year-old son, Fred, the work was carried on exclusively after dark, so that the wagons carrying away the debris would not attract attention.

At one end of the tube, in the basement of the building then standing at the corner of Warren Street and Broadway, a giant 100-horsepower blower was installed. By shifting the valves, the blower could be made to operate either as a blower or as an exhauster, either pushing or pulling the air in the tube. A single car was fitted into the tube, with a windage space of about an inch. The blower was turned on, and the car moved swiftly, but not uncomfortably, to the far end of the tube, under Murray Street. The valves were reversed and the blower promptly pulled the car back to Warren Street.

But Beach was not ready to show his subway as soon as it

was completed. A practical man with newspaper experience, he reasoned that to get away with his deception and win enough popular support to enable him to defy Boss Tweed, he needed a major Press send-off. So after digging his tunnel in less than two months, he spent the better part of two years giving it an elaborate, even luxurious interior finish. The station platform ran a good half the length of the tunnel, and was embellished by paintings, a goldfish tank, a fountain and even a grand piano, a lavishness unsurpassed by any subway built subsequently. The time taken for these refinements had the long-after incidental effect of confusing the date of the tunnel's construction. It is nearly always referred to in tunnelling literature as having been built in 1869, rather than 1868, an error of some importance, since the later date would make Beach's shield contemporaneous with Greathead's whereas it is actually earlier.

The Beach subway was a great popular success, but as anticipated it promptly drew the wrath of Boss Tweed, whose city administration threatened to shut it down. Beach took his case to Albany, where battle was soon joined in the legislature. Tweed presented a rapid-transit scheme of his own, a proposal for an elevated steam railway, mounted on massive stone piers—building materials being an important source of graft revenue for Tweed and his ring. The legislature approved both the Beach subway bill and the Tweed elevated bill; Governor John T. Hoffman, a Tweed man, vetoed the Beach bill and approved the Tweed bill.

Beach did not abandon the fight. Keeping his little showcase subway open, he had his bill brought to the floor again in the following year, 1872. It failed by one vote to pass over the governor's veto. The next year the Tweed Ring was smashed and a reform adminstration, headed by John A. Dix who served as a major-general during the Civil War, came into power in Albany. Beach's bill was triumphantly passed into law—but unluckily, the panic of 1873 hit almost simultaneously. The New York money market tightened up like a scared turtle, and financing a subway was out of the question. Governor Dix reluctantly cancelled the subway charter, whose time limit expired. The New York subway system was stopped in its tracks for a generation.

Actually Beach was working in a blind alley. Within a few

years the victorious arrival of electricity cancelled out the pneumatic tube as a transit motive power. Beach's idea was far from sterile, however, for pneumatic tubes were soon widely adopted by department stores to carry cash and sales slips between the counter and the cashier's office. Today they are still very much in use for the purpose which Beach originally conceived, that of carrying mail under large cities.

Beach himself continued to live a busy and fruitful life, remaining at the head of *Scientific American* till his death in 1896, the friend of Edison, Bell, Howe, Morse, and a thousand obscurer inventors. Edison is said to have first demonstrated his phonograph in Beach's office. Beach turned the crank and the machine said: "Good morning, sir. How are you? How do you like the talking box?"

Beach did not live to witness the New York subway era, but he employed the new telephone in a unique way to get around some of the inconveniences of a city without rapid transit. An admirer of Henry Ward Beecher, he found it impossible to make the long carriage trip to Brooklyn on Sunday, and so arranged with Beecher to have a private telephone wire connected to the pulpit and run to Beach's home on Twentieth Street in Manhattan. Sunday mornings he invited friends in and passed out earphones.

Several monuments remain to remind America of this practical and professorial genius. His 1868 tunnel is part of the BMT's City Hall Station, and a plaque there acknowledges his pioneer role in the greatest of all subway systems. His beloved *Scientific American,* which slumped to an insignificant position in the generation after his death, has taken on new life and vigour and became once more one of America's greatest and most influential publications. And the tunnelling shield which in America has always borne his name has dug under river after river and contributed more to solving the transportation problems of this busy nation than the pneumatic tube ever could have. Without the Beach (or Greathead) shield probably no American river could have been tunnelled successfully.

So casual was the invention of this indispensable tool that in 1874, the year after the little train under Broadway stopped running, it was apparently completely forgotten. "Mr. Beach was twenty years in advance of his time, and his inventions have acquired their fruition two or more decades after he originated them," was the explanation given by his own *Scientific American* in its obituary. But the truth is the shield was simply not adequately appreciated in 1874, in spite of the fact that it had been seized on by a Cleveland engineer to drive a water-supply tunnel out under Lake Erie. This was the first truly practical application of the cylindrical tunnel shield anywhere, for the Barlow-Greathead and Beach shields had driven their tunnels for experimental purposes. When New York undertook to tunnel under the Hudson River in 1874, the Beach shield was completely forgotten. Thereby hangs a tragic and moving story. The beautifully simple and effective device stood at the end of the Broadway tube, as if ready to recommence operations, while hardly a mile away a major tunnelling attempt ended in disaster for lack of a shield.

Before taking up the story of the Hudson Tubes, we must revisit the Alps, where in 1872 a new and terrifying chapter in mountain tunnelling was begun.

CHAPTER NINE

The St. Gothard: Speed and Death

One of the most picturesque and exciting train trips in the world is the two-hour ride on the Gothard Express through the Swiss Alps section of the Zurich-Milan run. Tunnels, then flashes of breath-taking scenery, more tunnels, more scenery, then suddenly the black drama of the great St. Gothard Tunnel, nine miles of rocketing through pitch darkness at one hundred kilometres an hour.

The trip is perfectly safe. Back in steam-engine days there was a certain hazard from coal gas and smoke—the engineers sometimes had to lie down on the floor of the engine cabs. Now it is merely exhilarating. Yet hundreds of men died to build this tunnel under one of the oldest and most storied of Alpine passes. From the sixth century a pack trail over Gothard existed; men and mules fought their way up and over the pass, and frequently froze to death or vanished under avalanches. The massif towers 3,000 metres above sea level; from its snowy slopes thread the icy mountain streams that grow into the Rhine, the Rhône, the Aar, and the Reuss Rivers. Only in the nineteenth century was the old pack trail widened into a wagon road—a road which was of course closed down tight all through the winter.

A tunnel through this mighty mass of ice-covered rock? In 1850 the idea was unthinkable. But in 1870, with Sommeiller's Italian gangs blasting ahead ten feet a day through Mont-Cenis, a tunnel through St. Gothard was not merely thinkable, it was so obvious that contractors were eagerly bidding for the job. The length of the Gothard tunnel would be longer than Mont-Cenis; the depth under the mountain would be greater; the dangers would necessarily be more serious. Yet once Sommeiller's drill, Nobel's explosive, and Colladon's compressed air had proven their powers, no one doubted that Gothard could be tunnelled too.

The demand was there. Mont-Cenis linked Italy and France,

the Mediterranean and the west. The St. Gothard would link Italy and Switzerland, the Mediterranean and the north. The Swiss Central Railway asked for bids, stressing the need for speed and economy in construction. No fewer than seven contracting firms entered bids. This competitive enthusiasm was dangerous rather than healthy. Of the seven contractors the choice narrowed to two: Signor Grattoni, head of the Italian Public Works Company, and Louis Favre of Geneva. Favre won the contract by promising a far lower price—48,000,000 francs as opposed to 60,000,000—and a quicker completion—within eight years. Favre's calculations were not unreasonable in the light of the Mont-Cenis experience, but they did not allow for any obstacles not encountered by Sommeiller. An average speed of eighty metres per month would suffice, and Sommeiller had achieved ninety metres in his best months at Mont-Cenis. Sommeiller's final costs had run to 5,500 francs per metre, considerably higher than anticipated, but the actual working costs for the final years, and especially the final months, when the tunnelling technique had been brought to a high pitch of efficiency, were far lower than this. It seemed reasonable to believe, in view of still further improvements in drilling machinery, use of dynamite throughout, a better system of clearing the debris, and especially what Favre believed to be an advantageous change in the location of the advance gallery, to anticipate a considerable improvement even over the final months' progress at Mont-Cenis.

At Mont-Cenis, the advance gallery had been driven at the base of the tunnel; Favre figured that he could gain time by driving it at the top instead. The work of the following crew would be more difficult, but he would solve this problem by employing a larger following crew, strung out over a greater length of tunnel. His attacking crew, in contrast, would be considerably smaller than Sommeiller's—some seventeen men compared with over sixty in the Mont-Cenis heading. Improvements on the Sommeiller drill were already being worked out; the drill holes would be deeper than on the Mont-Cenis, and a smaller number of charges per attack would be required. Also, his finishing crew would be equipped with light machine drills.

Favre called on his fellow Genevan, Professor Colladon, to design the air-compressor system; no fewer than fifteen compressors were installed at each heading. Colladon designed sheet-metal pipes with a new feature—the diameter narrowed as the pipes ran into the tunnel, to help maintain pressure at a distance. The wagons used to clear the debris would be hauled by compressed-air engines instead of horses.

The whole project, in fact, was far more carefully planned in advance than Mont-Cenis; there, the enterprise had had the flavour of a national and scientific venture; here the atmosphere was strictly business.

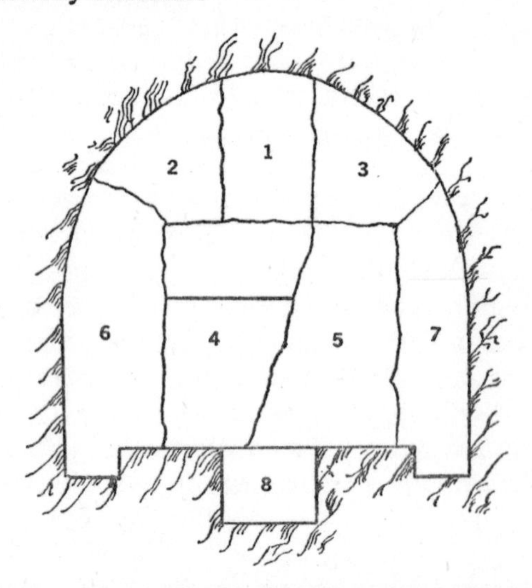

ST. GOTHARD: Cross-section, showing order of advance with top heading driven first. Lines around tunnel bore show angle of stress in the rock, which determined size and shape of numbered sections.

Work began late in 1872, at both headings. Progress was satisfactory, each attack yielded a little better than a metre, and the improved drills resulted in cutting the time per attack from twelve hours (at Mont-Cenis) to about eight. But a few weeks after the commencement of operations at the south heading a disturbing incident occurred; at 200 metres from the portal, water was encountered in the very considerable volume of 270 cubic metres per hour. The drainage canal was flooded, and water ran a foot deep in the heading. Within a few days the influx ceased.

In March of 1873 a new torrent burst into the south heading—this time at the truly formidable rate of 800 cubic metres per hour, knocking the labourers off their feet, carrying away tools, damaging the machinery and flooding the whole gallery. When the water had drained off, work was energetically resumed in an effort to regain the time. All went well till September, when another deluge of equal proportions once more brought a temporary halt at the south (Airolo) heading.

The next year, 1874, water inrushes came with great frequency, attaining 876 cubic metres (232,000 gallons) an hour and disrupting the work to such an extent that an advance of only 747 metres was registered for the year—a rate fatal to Favre's contract, which carried forfeit and premium clauses. If the tunnel was finished ahead of time, Favre stood to gain 5,000 francs per day; if on the other hand it was late he was committed to payment of 5,000 francs a day for six months and 10,000 francs a day after.

In 1875 multiple disasters struck. The labour force, some three thousand men strung out along the length of the two headings, began falling ill at a truly alarming rate. Two months was as long as most men worked at a stretch, and many of those falling ill refused to return to the tunnel.

An American visiting the work at this time write a vivid description. He rode in behind one of the little compressed-air engines:

> As we rushed by dripping walls, and saw here and there ghoul-like figures with dim lamps hiding behind rocks or in deep niches, I involuntarily recalled what our conductor had said of a glimpse of the bowels of hell.
>
> It was impossible to speak and be heard. I might as well have addressed myself to the granite walls or the tunnel as to have attempted a word to either of my companions. . . .
>
> We now started forward in the tunnel on foot and, as we recovered our breath, had abundant time to look about, though there seemed something fatally wrong with the perspective of the picture of which we formed a part.
>
> The air was so thick lights could not be seen twenty yards ahead of us, and we all walked close together for fear of being lost or tumbling into some subterranean hole.
>
> Far ahead of us we heard the dynamite explosions, sounding like heavy mortars in the midst of battle. In some places where we were walking the water was nearly a foot deep, and again it came through crevasses about our heads like April showers.

Noting that only Italians would accept tunnel labour under the prevailing conditions—three to six francs for an eight-hour day, no portal-to-portal—this observer, who wrote his account in *Harper's, New Monthly Magazine,* described the workmen's food:

> Their food is extremely limited in quantity, and is wretched in quality, consisting largely of polenta, or a sort of Indian meal porridge. Meat they never taste at all. They are contented to receive their forty or fifty cents a day for hard work, if they can only escape wounds and death from the bad gases and the thousand accidents to which they are liable every moment of their lives in the tunnel. Alas! They do not escape, for every week records its disaster, either from explosions and flying rocks, falling timbers and masonry, or railway accidents, breaking machinery, etc.

At one point the workers struck against the intolerable conditions, but the strike was broken without ceremony in that day of brutal labour policy. A guide who witnessed the episode, says:

> Then the Tessin soldiers came, and justly or not, fired on them (the workers on strike), and numbers of the poor fellows were killed or wounded. It was the only strike at the tunnel.

The dynamite was a menace every moment. At one point an explosion outside the tunnel blew several workmen so completely to pieces that "nothing of them save their heavy boots containing their mangled feet was ever found." And shortly after the strike a discharged worker threw a stick of dynamite into the company offices near the portal, completely demolishing them. By chance, none of the officials were in the offices.

Poor ventilation was the chief complaint, and the cause of the greatest mortality. Too much of Professor Colladon's compressed air had been allocated to the machinery and not enough to the men; the medical chief of the later Simplon tunnel calculated that the air requirement of one workman with his lamp was one-half cubic metre per minute. At St. Gothard less than half this amount was provided. But almost unquestionably the main contributor to the toll among Gothard tunnellers was a disease totally unknown to medical science—silicosis. The magnesium silicate under the peak had not been detected by the bore samples, but would hardly have caused alarm in any case. This soft rock, under drilling, produces a whitish dust which settles in the lungs; itself a killer, it also paves the way for other pulmonary diseases. It was not till well into the twentieth century that silicosis was well enough understood to apply the simple remedy of wet drilling in silicate rock.

Acrimony developed between Favre and Gerwig, chief engineer of the railway. Gerwig resigned and was replaced by a Danish engineer named Hellwag, but the troubles did not end. On July 28, 1875, when the south heading had progressed, despite all its difficulties, to a point over 2,000 metres from the Airolo portal, an inrush of water at 1,260 cubic metres per hour burst in.

As the two galleries inched deeper and deeper under the Gothard peak, temperatures rose in the headings, reaching 93° F. The work was pushed at the most rapid rate possible. Professor Colladon contributed a new invention, a compressed-air tender for steam locomotives to haul away the debris. Two new drills made their appearance, one in particular, the Ferroux, proving simpler, cheaper, and less susceptible of breakdowns than any previous devices. The dynamiting process was speeded up; in their enforced haste the workers often did not check the charges after a blast to make sure they had all fired properly, and numerous accidents resulted. A rate of advance of 130 metres a month was attained, compared with a maximum of ninety by Sommeiller at Mont-Cenis. But behind the heading the army of workers engaged in completing the excavation and constructing the masonry walls was strung out for a 1,000 metres, lagging more than a year behind the attacking crew. This situation, the result of Favre's method of construction, which was in turn the result of the contract's emphasis on speed, brought new misfortunes and very nearly disaster. A fresh enemy, rock swelling, suddenly made its ominous presence felt. Incomplete walls were crushed inward, crumpled by an enormous pressure of shifting weights in the mass above them. Favre blamed the company, which had made certain specifications about the thickness of the mortar, the type of timbering, etc., in the interests of economy. After some bickering, the company agreed to contribute to the cost of thicker walls in some places where collapses had occurred or threatened. Fresh collapses in the Andermatt in 1879 led to prescription of a new thickness of wall, two and a half metres.

On July 15, 1879, Favre himself fell victim to his tunnel. Overwork and worry brought on a heart attack which struck him down as he was emerging from the heading. For the past six months he had been virtually filling the role of chief engineer himself; now a new engineer, Bridel, was appointed by the company to finish the job. The headings were very nearly holed through; yet an enormous amount of work remained, and a fresh tragedy was already under way.

A serious epidemic had broken out among the workmen in the south heading the year before; now it appeared in the north. Its cause was a mystery, yet it operated with virulence in both the north and south headings; the hospitals around Goeschenen and Airolo were filled to overflowing, and the death rate was high. At last an autopsy revealed the murderer —a parasitic worm, *ankylostome*, which lived in water. In the insanitary conditions of the working gangs, it was easy to pass the infecting agent from man to man.

Despite all obstacles, the tunnel was holed through on February 29, 1880. The finishing crews, far behind the attacking party, did not complete their work until October 1881, with a consequent considerable forfeit by the contractor—or rather, his business heirs. Worse than the year's tardiness was the cost of construction, which ran perhaps a thousand francs over Favre's calculation of 3,208 francs per running metre.

Adding to the cost were the "spiral tunnels" which had to be built at each portal to lead the railway line up in gradually ascending loops with grades practical for locomotives.

Yet, despite all difficulties, foreseen and unforeseen, the St. Gothard Tunnel today remains a remarkable feat for its time. Given the experience of Mont-Cenis, it was understandable that Favre and his engineers failed to anticipate the floodings, the rock swellings and even the heat which they encountered.

The epidemics which broke out among the Gothard workmen directed salutary attention to the problem of tunnel hygiene. Yet given the general working conditions prevalent in the 1870s, and the normal attitude of management in that impetuous heyday of *laissez faire* capitalism—not to mention the state of medical knowledge—it would be unfair to attach too much blame to Favre and his associates for the disasters of the enterprise.

The hazards of tunnelling, in fact, were about to be brought home to the general public, as well as to tunnel engineers, in an even more dramatic adventure already unfolding across the Atlantic.

CHAPTER TEN

Trouble under the Hudson

In the nineteenth century, New York grew from a thriving small town of 60,000 population—and whose name many educated Europeans had never heard—into a metropolitan colossus whose teeming three and a half millions filled up Manhattan Island and overflowed all the surrounding shores.

Thanks to the Hudson River and the Erie Canal, New York left Boston and Philadelphia behind as an entrepôt for the American West. The railroad age did nothing to change the basic geographic and topographic advantages of New York. The Hudson Valley and the plain of western New York State provided ideal railroad grounds, save for a solitary obstacle—the Hudson itself. From the point of view of freight transport, the obstacle was not significant by mid-century. Freight could be transferred to river barges and brought to shipping piers quite conveniently. But passenger traffic across the river was already reaching a critical stage; despite the efficacy of the ferry-boat fleet there was a very evident need for a means of carrying railroad passenger traffic directly into New York. For the engineering art of the mid-nineteenth century a bridge at this point posed virtually insoluble problems, not only was the Hudson here a mile wide and seventy feet deep, but it was known to have a deep mud bottom. No bridge in fact existed for 145 miles upstream from Manhattan until the Poughkeepsie bridge was constructed in 1889.

But Brunel's tunnel under the Thames had been completed in 1841, and in mid-century American engineers might well ask, was it not possible to tunnel under the Hudson? The river, at Manhattan Island, was a far more formidable stream than the Thames, and Brunel's experience was not exactly reassuring. But Brunel had worked without compressed air, and that powerful tunnelling tool had now proved its mettle. The Civil War, a momentary brake on many engineering enterprises, very soon by the tremendous impetus it gave to industrial development stimulated enormous new transportation efforts—railroad, road, street railways, with their bridges and tunnels.

In 1870 a former Union Army officer from the West conceived a brilliant and daring solution—compressed air. Colonel DeWitt Clinton Haskins had examined and admired the technique by which the famous engineer James Buchanan Eads had bridged the Mississippi River at St. Louis by sinking caissons full of compressed air in which men could work at the river bottom. The technique was not original with Eads; it had been invented and patented by a British engineer named Sir Thomas (later Lord) Cochrane back in 1830. Cochrane had designed an air-lock to solve the problem of admitting men to the compressed-air caisson, with an outer door opening inward and an inner door opening outward into the compressed-air chamber. Through this air-lock Cochrane, and afterwards Eads and other bridge engineers, took their workmen and materials. The very first use of it was by a French engineer named Triger who sank a caisson through quicksand in the Loire; later it was used on many bridges in Britain and Ireland.

Cochrane had not thought of using compressed air for tunnelling, though Professor Colladon, the great Genevan had suggested compressed air to Brunel during the Thames tunnelling, as a means of keeping the face of the working dry.

To Haskins, noting the air-lock and iron rings Eads used under the Mississippi, the notion occurred that if the air-lock were placed at the portal of an under-river tunnel, and if the iron rings were used to line the tunnel, the problem of the Hudson would be solved.

Arrived in New York, Haskins at once sought financial support for tunnelling under the Hudson by his method, and with the aid of a financier named Trenor W. Park he presently raised $10,000,000 capitalization for the Hudson Tunnel Railroad Company.

Since the river bottom did not vary appreciably in the North River area, the tunnel's location was governed by convenience, which dictated a portal on the New York side at Morton Street, then near the centre of the city. The New Jersey terminus was fixed at a point on Hudson Street, Jersey City, between the Erie and the Delaware and Lackawanna Railroads. Haskins's plan was simple. Instead of employing a shield, as had Brunel and Greathead, he would merely maintain an air pressure in the heading proportionate to the hydrostatic head—the total weight of water above. Together with ordinary timbering he felt this would enable him to hold the iron plates securely in place until the masonry could be built. Simple, and ingenious, and certainly daring—in effect, Haskins sought to hold up the Hudson River by a tunnel full of compressed air. Theoretically, the plan was perfectly sound, and one of the distinctive characteristics of the great nineteenth-century engineering adventurers was their readiness to gamble on the translation of theory into practice. In November 1874, a shaft thirty-eight feet in diameter was begun on the New Jersey side and sunk to a depth of sixty feet. At this point the first of Haskins's troubles arose. The Delaware, Lackawanna and Western Railroad, which operated a ferry at Christopher Street, just above the route of the proposed tunnel, obtained an injunction to stop the work. Because of this and other lawsuits, work could not be recommenced till September 1879. That very year an apparently happy augury for Haskins's project came from abroad; Hersent, contractor for the extensive dock works in the Scheldt being constructed for the port of Antwerp, successfully used compressed air to drive an "adit," or small tunnel, under the estuary.

Within two months the New Jersey shaft had reached down to the sand stratum; immediately water began pouring in at the rate of 200 gallons a minute. Pumps soon mastered the situation, but at a cost, for the removal of so much water caused the ground all around the shaft to alter considerably. Nonetheless the shaft was carried down to the predetermined depth of sixty feet. From here the tunnel would descend by a gentle grade to under midstream, then rise again towards the New York side.

Down the finished shaft was lower Haskins's prized tunnelling tool—the air-lock. This was a cylinder of boiler-plate iron fifteen feet long and six feet in diameter. In each end was a door three feet wide by four high, with a small bull's-eye window. That on the shaft side opened inward; that on the tunnel side outward. This cylinder was fixed in place in a concrete bulkhead at the point where the horizontal shaft was to begin and work commenced. The men descended the vertical shaft, entered the air-lock, and waited until the pressure was raised to twelve pounds per square inch, sufficient to equal the relatively low pressure of water at this shallow edge of the river. When equalization of pressure had been achieved, the tunnel-side door was opened and the men began digging. Thereafter, pressure was maintained inside the heading and first results vindicated Haskins's theory; the air held back the water, and the silt contained the air, long enough to permit wooden timbering followed by the installation of a series of iron rings which were then completed by masonry. After the first beginnings, two parallel single-track tunnels were projected rather than a single large bore.

One day a workman who had come out of the shaft at the end of his shift was suddenly bent double in a violent spasm of agony. He was rushed to a hospital, where the symptoms were immediately recognized as a dread new affliction called by the doctors caisson disease and soon to be named by sandhogs "the bends."

Unluckily, the disease was very badly understood, despite the fact that it had been observed for a considerable period in Europe and that its cure had actually been discovered. Back in 1839, when Triger sank his caisson in the Loire quicksand, he had noted workmen suffering pain after leaving compression. A few years later two other French engineers who sank a mine shaft near Valenciennes used pressures of up to forty-eight pounds above atmospheric and made the important observation that incidence of illness was proportionate to speed of decompression. These two men, Pol and Watelle, tried recompression for stricken workmen, and found that it gave relief. A few years later, in 1863, a Dr. Foley reported on compressed-air sickness—to give the disease its modern medical name—in England, and also prescribed slow decompression, and return to compression for victims. On the Eads Bridge over the Mississippi which Haskins had admired, pressures of up to fifty pounds had been used, with numerous fatal cases of illness; at one point six deaths were recorded in ten days. In 1873, Dr. Andrew H. Smith, a young surgeon for the Brooklyn Bridge project, also corroborated these observations, but a real insight into the cause of the disease was still lacking. Furthermore, the attitude towards tunnel workers' lives was not much different in Jersey City from that in Switzerland.

The tunnel was pushed inflexibly on. The heading was

driven at the top until a new iron plate could be put in, bolted to the adjacent one. Then while the top gallery was advanced another step, the centre of the tunnel was excavated a step behind, and the bottom part another step behind, so that the heading consisted of roughly three huge steps, each about the height of a man. The excavation of the soft silt was carried out easily enough with picks and shovels, the mud taken away in wagons. At first the rate of advance was only about a foot a day, but as the men became accustomed to the job the advance speeded up to about five feet a day. Of the working crew of about thirty, three or four were always detailed to watch for leaks—escaping air which would open a hole through the silt to the river above. Whenever a leak was suspected, a lighted candle was held close to the spot; the flame drawn into the hole by the escaping air would pinpoint the danger. Sandbags were kept inside the tunnel for plugging.

Removal of excavated silt was done by a novel method; first the mud was mixed with water in a trough, then it was fed into a six-inch pipe and forced to the surface by the air pressure in the heading.

Progress continued to be good for several months, but the lines and grades were irregular. When the advance heading was pushed too far ahead of the finishing masonry, the slight variations in pressure between the air in the tunnel and the water-silt column above it distorted the iron rings. It was as if two giants were pressing, from inside and from out, against a tin shell: in general their pressures were equal, but from moment to moment the outer giant exerted more or less weight, and the inner giant failing to keep exact measure with him, the cylinder was squashed downward or pressed upward, with corresponding changes in the sides.

On July 21, 1880, the north tunnel had been completed for a distince of 300 feet under the river. Pressure in the heading was seventeen pounds per square inch. At four-thirty in the morning, one half of the men had returned to work and the other half had started for the air-lock for their period of rest, when one of them spotted a leak in the side of the shaft. This was not in itself an unusual occurrence, but this leak was suddenly transformed into a tragedy. One of America's greatest writers has described what followed in a memorable short story:

"Ssst!"

What was that? A sound like the blowing off of steam. All at once Cavanaugh, who was just outside indicating to McGlathery and another just where certain braces were to be put . . . heard it. At a bound he was back, his face aflame with fear and rage. . . .

"Come now! What the hell is this?" he was about to exclaim, but seeing a wide breach suddenly open and water pour down in a swift volume, his spirit sank and fear overcame him.

"Back, men! Stop the leak!"

It was the cry of a frightened and yet courageous man at bay. There was not only fear, but disappointment in it. He had certainly hoped to obviate anything like this. But where a moment before had been a hole that might have been stopped with a bag of sawdust (and Patrick Murtha was there attempting to do it) was now a rapidly widening gap through which was pouring a small Niagara of foul river water, ooze and slime. As Cavanaugh reached it and seized a bag to stay it, another mass of muddy earth fell, striking both him and Murtha, and half blinding them both. Murtha scrambled away for his life. McGlathery, who had been out in the front of the others, now came staggering back, horribly frightened, scarcely knowing what to do.

"Quick, Dennis! Into the lock!" Cavanaugh called to him, while he himself held his ground. "Hurry!" And realizing the hopelessness of it and his own danger, Dennis thought to run past, but was stopped by the downpour of water and mud.

"Quick! Quick! Into the lock! For Christ's sake, can't ye see what's happenin'? Through with ye!"

McGlathery, hesitating by his chief's side, fearful to move lest he be killed, uncertain this time whether to leave his chief or not, was seized by Cavanaugh and literally thrown through, as were others after him, the blinding ooze and water choking them, but placing them within range of safety. When the last man was through, Cavanaugh himself plunged after, wading knee-deep in mud and water.

"Quick! Quick! Into the lock!" he called, and then seeing McGlathery, who was now near it but waiting for him, added, "In, in!" There was a mad scramble about the door, floating timbers and bags interfering with many, and then, just as it seemed as if all would reach safety, an iron roof plate overhead, loosened by the breaking of plates beyond, gave way, felling one man in the half-open doorway of the lock and blocking and pinning it in such a way that it could be neither opened nor closed. Cavanaugh and others who came up after were shut out. McGlathery, who had just entered and saw it could no nothing. But in this emergency, and unlike his previous attitude, he and several others on the inside seized upon the dead man and tried to draw him in, at the same time calling to Cavanaugh to know what to do. The latter, dumbfounded, was helpless. He saw very clearly and sadly that very little if anything could be done. The plate across the dead man was too heavy, and besides, the ooze was already pouring over him into the lock. At the same time the men in the lock, conscious that although they were partially on the road to safety they were still in danger of losing their lives, were frantic with fear.

Actually, there were animal roars of terror . . . McGlathery . . . was completely paralysed with fear. . . .

"Holy Mary! Holy St. Columba!" he began to pray, "what shall I do now? Mother of God!"

As he gibbered and chattered, the others screaming about him, some pulling at the dead man, others pulling at the other door, the still eye of Cavanaugh outside the lock, waist-deep in mud and water, was surveying it all.

"Listen to me, men!" came his voice in rich, heavy, guttural tones. "You, McGlathery! Dennis! Take off yer clothes and stop up the doorway! It's yer only chance! Off with yer clothes, quick! And those planks there—stand them up! Never mind us. Save yerselves first. Maybe ye can do something for us afterwards."

His voice, commanding, never quavering, even in the face of death, subsided. About and behind him were a dozen men huddled like sheep, waist-deep in mud and water, praying and crying. They had got as close to him as might be, still trying to draw upon the sustaining force of his courage, but moaning and praying just the same and looking at the lock.

"Yes! Yes!" exclaimed McGlathery of a sudden, awakening at last to a sense of duty and that something better in conduct and thought which he had repeatedly promised himself and his saint that he would achieve. . . . Tearing off his coat and vest and shirt as commanded, he began pushing them into the opening, calling to the others to do the same. In a twinkling, bundles were made of all as well as of the sticks and beams afloat in the lock, and with these the gap in the door was stuffed, sufficiently to prevent the air from escaping, but shutting out the foreman and his men completely.

"It's awful. I don't like to do it," McGlathery kept crying to his foreman but the latter was not so easily shaken.

"It's all right, boys," he kept saying. "Have ye no courage at all?" And then to the others outside with him. "Can't ye stand still and wait? They may be comin' back in time. Keep still. Say yer prayers if ye know any, and don't be afraid."

But, although the air pressing outward towards Cavanaugh held the bundles in place, still this was not sufficient to keep all the air in or all the water out. It poured about the dead man and between the chinks, rising inside to their waists. Once more it threatened their lives and now their one hope was to pull open the shoreward door and so release themselves into the chamber beyond, but this was not to be done unless the escaping air was completely blocked or some other method devised.

Cavanaugh, on the outside, his whole mind still riveted on the men whom he was thus aiding to escape, was the only one who realized what was to be done. In the panel of the door which confronted him, and the other, which they were trying to break open, were thick glass plates, or what were known as bull's eyes, through which one could see, and it was through the one at his end that Cavanaugh was peering. When it became apparent to him that the men were not going to be able to open the farthest door, a new thought occurred to him. Then it was that his voice was heard above the tumult, shouting:

"Break open the outside bull's eye! Listen to men, Dennis! Listen to me! Break open the outside bull's eye! "

. . . Through a bedlam of cries within, McGlathery heard, but also realized that if he or they knocked out the bull's eye in the inner door, and the air escaped through it, the chances of their opening the door would be improved, but the life of Cavanaugh and his helpless companions would certainly be destroyed. The water would rush inward from the river, filling up this chamber and the space in which stood Cavanaugh. He hesitated.

"Knock it out! " came the muffled voice of his foreman. "Knock it out, Dennis! It's yer only chance! Knock it out! " And then, for the first time in all the years he had been working for him, McGlathery heard the voice of his superior waver slightly: "If ye're saved," it said, "try and do what ye can fer the rest of us."

. . . He looked about, saw a great stave, and seized it.

"Here, men! " he called with an air of command. "Help knock it out! " and with a will born of terror and death a dozen brawny hands were laid on it. With a mighty burst of energy they assaulted the thick plate and burst it through. Air rushed in, and at the same time the door gave way before them, causing them to be swept outward by the accumulated water like straws. Then, scrambling to their feet, they tumbled into the next lock, closing the door behind them . . . McGlathery turned and looked through the bull's eyes. . . . He saw in the chamber they had left his foreman and a dozen fellow workers buried beyond. . . .

" 'Tis the will of God," he murmured humbly—but why had God done that?*

In his fictional account, Theodore Dreiser took certain liberties with the details of the disaster, and some of his technical information is slightly at fault. He refers to air pressures of 2,000 pounds per square inch, apparently thinking of 2,000 pounds per square foot. But in the main his picture is as authentic as it is moving. The heroic foreman, whom Dreiser names Cavanaugh, was actually Peter Woodland, who perished with twenty workers, calmly directing the operation which saved the men in the air-lock while destroying his own chance of survival.

The blow was the all-but-inevitable result of the method Haskins used. Maintaining sufficient pressure to hold out the water was no problem; the difficulty lay in keeping this pressure high enough and yet not so high that it might not burst through a soft pocket in the mud overhead. This was what happened on the fatal night. The air began escaping upward through the mud at a point close to the air-lock, actually not under the river at all, but under the "made ground" near the river's edge. This "made ground," the result of filling in around the vertical shaft, was soft, porous, waterlogged. Also, the brick lining of the tunnel was only begun—the iron roof plates were secured only by the air pressure and their own interlinking. As the air escaped, lowering the pressure, a sudden strain was put on the roof. Mud and water seeped rapidly through. This action again compressed the remaining air, which then burst upward again in another huge bubble. The next reaction from above wrenched a cast-iron plate loose and sent it crashing down, killing one man, jamming the air-lock door and dooming the heroic Peter Woodland and his men.

The crowd of spectators who came running up above, halted in horror at the edge of a huge pool of black water which stood silently where the "made ground" had sunk.

Yet the tunnel was not abandoned. After the initial shock

*Reprinted by permission of The World Publishing Company from *The Best Short Stories of Theodore Dreiser*. Copyright 1927 by Theodore Dreiser. Copyright 1955 by Helen Dreiser.

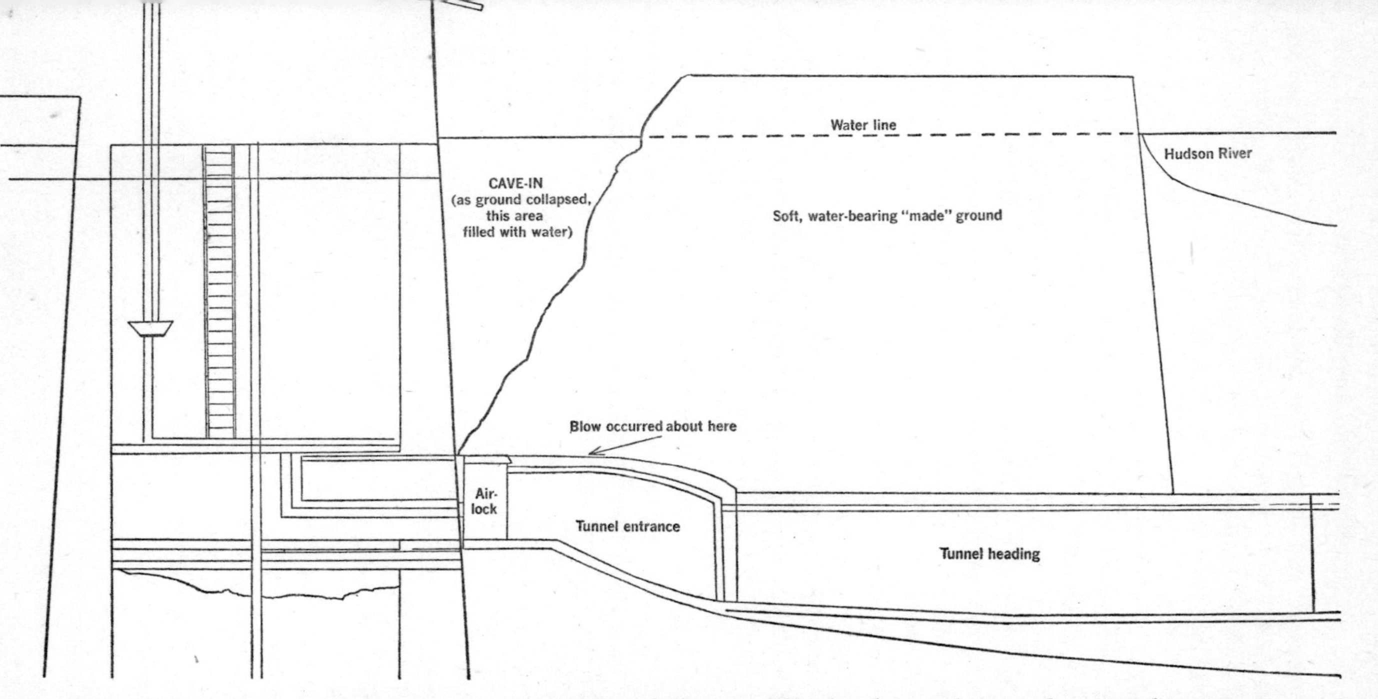

DISASTER UNDER THE HUDSON RIVER: Air pressure blew a hole in the roof near the tunnel entrance, under soft, waterlogged ground. As water and mud poured through the hole, falling timbers jammed the air-lock door, cutting off the escape of twenty men.

the tunnellers set doggedly to work again. By strenuous and complex efforts the heading was cleared, the bodies recovered, and the air-lock put back in working order. The tragedy had demonstrated the failure of Haskins's original technique. The "made ground" could be remade more solidly. But what was to prevent a blow at the front of the heading, out under the river, where there were not even any iron rings to hold up the roof? Nothing, obviously.

But Haskins's chief engineer, a Swede named John Anderson, but forward an ingenious suggestion, which was immediately adopted. A small advance heading was driven a few feet in front of the main tunnel, lined with iron rings. This method proved so successful that it was patented as "Anderson's Pilot Tube"; progress of five feet a day was again achieved.

A shaft was now sunk on the Manhattan side of the river, but work from here progressed slowly through gravel and sand.

On August 20, 1882, a new blowout occurred in the Jersey heading. The workmen, warned by the hissing sound of escaping air, made it to the air-lock, and no lives were lost. The tunnel, however, received another damaging blow to its reputation. Haskins's funds were running out, and he found it impossible to gain new backing for his hazard-ridden project.

Probably it was just as well. As the heading reached farther under the river, and pressure consequently increased, fatalities from the bends increased to the staggering rate of 25 per cent per year. The tunnel under the Hudson, driven by compressed air alone, was a ghastly failure.

London was the first city to develop an underground railway system. *(Right)* A contemporary cross-sectional engraving of the first underground rail tunnel, that of the Metropolitan Railway, opened in 1863, near what is now Euston Square Station. *(Below)* Liverpool Street, one of London's earliest underground stations, as it was fifty years ago, looking much as it does today

Marc Isambard Brunel's tunnel under the Thames, begun in 1825 and finished in 1843. *(Above)* A drawing made in 1856, before the tunnel was absorbed into the London underground. Intended for pedestrians, the tunnel was equipped with spiral flights of stairs at both ends. *(Below)* While some men worked at the shield others cleared away the excavated material and built the tunnel lining

(Below) The entrance to the Saint Gothard Tunnel through the Swiss Alps, constructed between 1872 and 1881 with the aid of an improved form of the compressed-air drill first used on the Mont-Cenis Tunnel. The Saint Gothard is nine miles long. A rate of advance of 120 yards per month was once attained during its construction, even though the working temperature rested at 34° C

A pony cart drawn on rails bringing back excavated material from the shield-face. This photograph was taken during the development of New York's early subway system but it was a common tunnelling sight both in Europe and America one hundred years ago

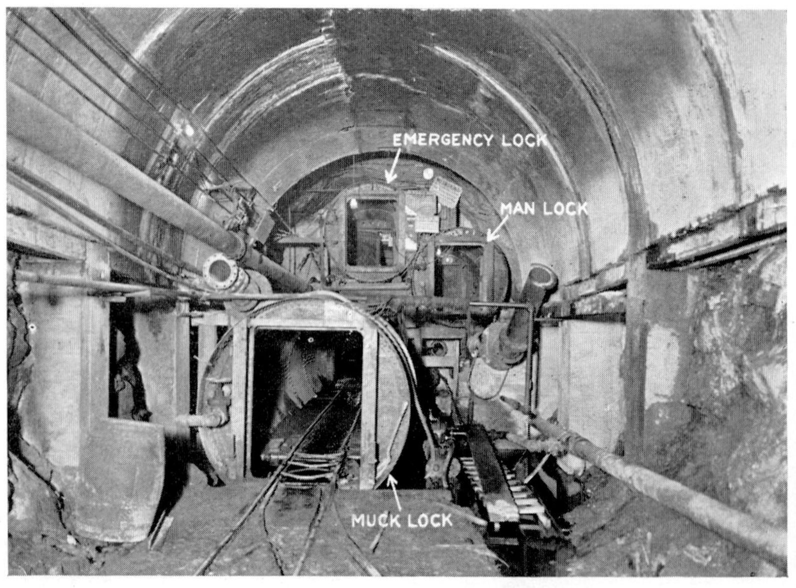

Together with a shield and compressed-air drilling equipment modern tunnellers often make use of three separate air-locks built into an air-lock bulkhead: the muck lock, for bringing out the excavated material; the man lock, for the workmen to pass through; and the emergency lock

CHAPTER ELEVEN

James Henry Greathead Solves the River Problem

Alfred Beach was the first man to build a cylindrical tunnel shield. To the best of this author's knowledge, this fact is set down in this book for the first time, for all the old tunnelling authorities have credited another man entirely with the first cylindrical shield. The question is interesting but academic. Alfred Beach was a many-sided genius. But the man who made shield tunnelling a success, not merely by designing a shield but by using it effectively—and above all, *by using it with compressed air*—was a South African-born British engineer named James Henry Greathead.

This remarkable man had been sent to England at the age of fifteen in 1859 to complete his education, which he had done under the tutelage of Peter William Barlow, one of the greatest engineers in a country of engineers. Barlow was concerned with the problem of operating railways inside the metropolitan area of London, and had conceived a daring solution: a system of underground railways running in cast-iron tubes. We shall take up the underground in a later chapter; of immediate interest is Barlow's solution for tunnelling under the Thames. In 1864 he patented a cylindrical shield of his own design and in 1868 proposed the construction of a small-diameter tunnel under the Thames as a demonstration of the validity of his theory. Greathead, then just twenty-four years old, promptly volunteered to drive the tunnel for the sum of £9,400.

Years later there was some coolness, if not acrimony, between Greathead and Peter Barlow's nephew over credit for the Tower underground. Greathead asserted at a meeting of the British Institution of Civil Engineers that he had known nothing of Barlow's shield patent of 1864. In any case, Greathead designed and constructed a shield weighing two and a half tons, with a diameter of seven feet one and three-quarter inches, sank it in a shaft opposite the Tower of London and pushed out under the river. The shield was advanced by screw jacks, and the tunnel lined with cast-iron rings in segments, with apertures to permit cement grouting. All these features had been included in Barlow's patents of 1864 and '68; a significant feature which was indisputably Greathead's own was his location of the door in the "diaphragm" or face. Barlow had placed the door in the middle; Greathead put it in the upper half; his purpose was to provide for using compressed air to exclude water from the upper half of the heading in front of the shield, and so making it workable.

At the depth chosen—twenty-two feet minimum below the river bottom—the Thames clay proved strong and impermeable, and no compressed air was needed. A workman would squeeze through the door, dig away a space in front of the shield, passing the material back through the diaphragm door. Then he would retreat through the opening himself, the door would be closed and six men, turning six handles, would cause six rams, braced against the tunnel lining, to force the shield forward a foot and a half.

The 1,350-foot distance was negotiated in the astonishing time of five months, at a cost of less than £10,000. Though the tunnel bore was only a twentieth of the mighty Brunel tunnel, it was a very striking demonstration of the potential of the cylindrical shield. The only difficulty encountered was with the grouting; the cement had to be reduced to so liquid a state in order to be squirted by syringe into the grouting holes that it tended to run off instead of drying in place behind the iron rings. Greathead solved this problem for future tunnellers by designing a compressed-air grouting pan which could be operated easily by two men.

But the most important feature of the Tower underground was the one that existed only in Greathead's imagination—compressed-air tunnelling. Greathead had not only anticipated DeWitt Haskins; he had correctly foreseen that compressed air could be safely used only in conjunction with the shield.

Five years later, at the very time that DeWitt Haskins was sinking his shaft in Jersey City, Greathead patented a new shield, expressly designed for compressed-air tunnelling under loose, water-bearing strata. Greathead's new shield was to be used for a projected tunnel under the Thames at Woolwich, a plan which was abandoned. But a few years later another

Thames tunnel was projected, to connect the City (downtown London) with Clapham on the south side of the Thames. The tunnel was to be part of the London Underground system, commenced back in 1856, but heretofore dug only in the solid clay under the metropolis's cobbled streets. The new undertaking, involving a pair of railway tunnels at the Monument, was at first called the London and Southwark Railway, and subsequently known as the City and South London Railway. It was authorized by Parliament in 1884, and work was begun in October 1886.

The first tunnel was begun behind the Old Swan Pier, near

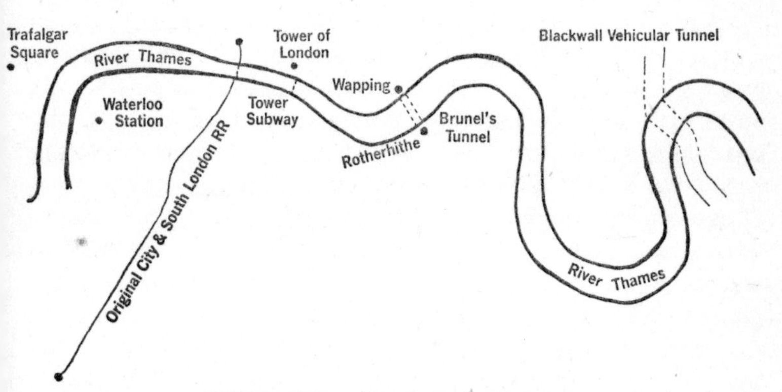

TUNNELLING UNDER THE THAMES

London Bridge. Its companion was begun the following March, and by June both tunnels were finished. The success of the operation was such that it has scarcely any history. The technique employed by Greathead was four-step:

1. Workmen opened the doors in front of the shield and dug a "box heading," four by six feet, a short distance in front of the shield.

2. The top and bottom of this heading, immediately in front of the shield, were excavated for a couple of feet, and the shield moved forward by its six hydraulic rams.

3. Behind the tail of the shield the half-ton segments forming the cast-iron rings were fixed in place by a hydraulic "erector"—a giant steel arm and hand.

4. The lining was sealed with the aid of Greathead's compressed-air grouting pan.

So easy, in fact, was the operation that the full merits of the Greathead system were actually concealed. The river bottom proved to be solid London clay, impervious to water, and no water was encountered until the first tunnel was driven northward from its shaft to make the connection with the rest of the underground line. Here water was suddenly encountered. The shield face was closed and progress continued under compressed air. The soft pocket lasted only fifty yards, but this marked the very first use of shield and compressed air in combination.

The river tunnel was of course only a part of the whole operation of constructing the City and South London Railway. Altogether eighteen Greathead shields, with slightly varying designs, were used. Parliament would not grant easements for passing under buildings, and in fact an important cost stipulation was that the buildings not be disturbed. Consequently the tunnel was pushed under the streets, and speed of advance became a major objective to avoid collapsing nearby walls. Greathead designed shields which could be easily manœuvred to turn laterally with the windings of the streets, by manipulating the pressure on the rams on the right or left side. To gain maximum speed he added steel wedges fixed to the front of the shield, which dug into the clay as the shield was driven forward. In the second half of 1888, six working faces accounted for an average advance of eighty feet a day.

Water-bearing strata were encountered in several places, most notably near Stockwell, where the tunnel was driven two hundred yards under a head of thirty-five feet of water. Compressed air at fifteen pounds per square inch above the atmosphere was used, with prompt lining and grouting, and no difficulties were encountered. Nor were any ill effects reported among the workmen at this moderate pressure.

But Greathead's demonstration of the effectiveness of the shield combined with compressed air had immediate repercussions. Before the City and South London was finished, three important new subaqueous tunnelling enterprises were under way—including a renewal of effort under the Hudson.

E. W. Moir Fights the "Bends"

The confident British now turned their eyes across the Atlantic. Sir Benjamin Baker, one of the most distinguished engineers in London, came over to New York to have a look at Haskins's tunnel. The examination of the tunnel which he made in company of Haskins's nephew was very nearly disastrous; on returning from the heading the two men found it impossible completely to shut the inner door of the air-lock. Consequently, when they opened the valve which released air through the outer door (on the shore side), the pressure in the lock did not diminish and the outer door would not open. For some time the two men were in a serious dilemma; if they allowed too much air to escape, the heading would collapse and fill the air-lock not with air but with water and silt. Yet it was impossible to pull open the inner door against the pressure of the compressed air. Finally they hit on the expedient of digging mud from the heading, bringing it into the air-lock and smearing the door opening. The crack was closed sufficiently to permit them to reduce the pressure a little in the lock, and at last force the outer door open. Despite this alarming experience, Sir Benjamin returned an optimistic report to London, asserting his opinion that the tunnel could be completed if a shield were employed.

Capital was at once raised in London (though as the event proved not enough), Greathead was consulted, and the construction of a shield, to Sir Benjamin's specifications, entrusted to a young engineer named E. W. Moir, then working on the great Firth of Forth Bridge. A contract was let to S. Pearson and Sons, and Moir appointed chief engineer.

Moir's first task was to erect his shield—2,000 feet under the river. Compressed air at thirty-five pounds per square inch had to be used, and cases of bends began appearing at once, with several fatalities.

As we have seen, some European and American doctors and engineers had observed that men suffering from caisson disease could be relieved by a return to compression. Moir resolved to provide for such treatment by erecting a special "homeopathic air chamber" at the top of the Jersey City shaft. When a man was attacked by the bends after emerging from the shaft, he was placed in this lock, at the same pressure under which he had been working. Experience showed that the optimum pressure for recovery was actually about two-thirds the working pressure; if this was then reduced at a rate of about a pound a minute, at the end of twenty-five or thirty minutes atmospheric pressure was reached and the victim could walk out in good condition. The air chamber reduced the death rate from one per month—out of a working gang of fifty—to two deaths in the whole remaining fifteen months of work, out of a crew of 120. Among others Moir's own boss, Sir Weetman Pearson, the contractor, was cured of paralysis by the air-lock treatment.

Apart from the bends, the work progressed excellently. The shield was not "entered" for working, but simply pushed forward through the soft mud by its hydraulic rams. The mud squeezed back through the small shield door (two and a half by two feet) at a rate twelve times that of the shield's advance. Most of the water was squeezed out by the process and the hard mud could be picked up inside the face in great lumps.

In about a year and a half, Moir advanced the shield 1,900 feet, to within 1,600 feet of the Manhattan heading. At this point a financial panic in London suddenly cut off funds and forced abandonment of the work for the third time since Haskins's commencement. This time the tunnel was to wait twelve long years. Meantime, 700 miles west, another under-river tunnel was being pushed successfully to a conclusion—actually the first under-river tunnel successfully driven by compressed air.

The St. Clair Tunnel:

The Canadian Grand Trunk Railway needed a tunnel under the St. Clair River, at Sarnia and Port Huron, to supplant its ferry and make a direct link with rail lines in Michigan. Greathead's success with the City and South London inspired confidence that a heading could be driven under the St. Clair 2,300 feet wide at this point, by use of shield and compressed air. The two shields used, however, were actually modelled after Alfred Beach's Broadway shield of twenty years earlier. Assembled on the site, one on each side of the river, the shields were rolled down inclined planes to the tunnel mouths, well back from the river. Air pressure was begun shortly after commencement, at about ten pounds, gradually raised to twenty-eight pounds by the time the centre of the river was reached. Within a few months a rate of advance of twelve feet a day had been achieved on the American side. Three eight-hour shifts a day were worked in both headings, with twenty-five men per shift. The total length of tunnel bored was six thousand feet, and the tunnel was finished within two years.

The cost of both the shields, built in the United States, and the cast-iron lining—which accounted for a third of the whole expenditure—was well justified by the rapid and accident-free completion.

Greathead's principles had now been incontestably proven. For the first time, an important tunnel had been driven under a wide river by shield and compressed air. More soon followed.

Fidler's Ferry Aqueduct

Contemporary with the St. Clair tunnel was a British project to carry water to Liverpool under the Mersey River. This was the Vyrnwy Aqueduct, driven at Fidler's Ferry in 1888. Shafts were sunk to place the tunnel 100 feet below high water, with the hope of boring through boulder clay and dispensing with shield and compressed air. But after eighteen months' effort, only sixty feet had been dug out of a total length of 805. The contractor quit. The variability of the material, and the many water inrushes, which could not be contained even by compressed air, seemed beyond handling.

Greathead was consulted. On his advice a completely new heading was started only fifty feet below high water, using a shield and compressed air. The first shield still permitted too much water to enter, and a new modification was introduced—a "trap" at the bottom of the shield. Two methods were used to advance. If air was escaping evenly through the face, keeping it dry, men dug out a space eighteen inches in front of the shield diaphragm, and the shield was shoved. If the air was escaping unevenly, so that the face was wet, the men worked from within the shield, and enough pressure was kept on the rams to keep pushing the shield forward with each spadeful of earth removed, until an advance of eighteen inches had been achieved. Then work was suspended till a new iron ring could be emplaced. With these innovations, work was finished in 1890.

Forty-eight Pounds of Pressure under the East River

But the most difficult of all the compressed-air operations carried out in the '90s was back in New York. This tunnel was on Manhattan's other side—under the East River. The

East River Gas Company of Long Island wanted to extend its operations to the main part of the city. The only practical way of carrying gas to Manhattan was by tunnel under the river. The dangers of such a project were realized, but the motivation was strong, for unlike some nineteenth-century tunnels, this one promised sure profits from packed Manhattan's gas-hungry dwellings.

To study the feasibility of the operation, Charles M. Jacobs, a young British engineer who had come to New York with Pearson and Moir, was engaged, Jacobs encountered an initial trouble in taking adequate bore samples in the traffic-crowded East River, but had no difficulty selecting an ideal route—directly under Blackwells Island, now Welfare Island, a two-mile-long sliver which divides the East River into a pair of narrow, deep, and swift-running channels. Maximum depth at high tide, seventy-one feet, current nine knots, minimum tunnel cover forty feet, a combination spelling serious hazards if the bottom was not bedrock. And the bore samples, though showing "New York rock"—a solid micaceous gneiss composing and underlying Manhattan Island—for most of the way, gave evidence of possible more treacherous material.

Nonetheless, Jacobs felt certain the tunnel could be driven. The company appointed him chief engineer and ordered work begun. Jacobs commissioned a private contracting firm, McLaughlin and Reilly, to sink shafts on both sides of the river and bore a small tunnel—eight feet in diameter, enough to carry three gas mains. The total under-river distance was 2,500 feet, including 800 feet under the island. The Manhattan shaft was begun June 28, 1892, at a point between 70th and 71st Streets just west of what is now the East River Drive. Shortly after, the Long Island shaft was begun at Ravenswood. The shafts did not descend as rapidly as Jacobs wished, but in October the Manhattan shaft was turned and the tunnel begun.

For 348 feet from the Manhattan shore the "New York rock" held, and tunnelling was done in the Alpine fashion—drilling and explosives—with no thought of compressed air. Suddenly one day in December, salt water poured into the heading. The East River of course is not a river but a strait, and the saline quality of the water meant that the tunnellers had struck a vein of material that the river could freely penetrate. Under the Hudson the silt was soft in the sense that strong pressure was needed to hold it up, but it was impervious to the passage of water.

An advance heading was driven a few feet, while the pumps were put to work, but as the heading progressed into constantly softer material, consisting of decomposed feldspar and other rock, water entered in such quantities that it dug a pocket in front of the hastily erected bulkhead. This action was carried out in a series of rushes, accompanied by formidable bubbling noises which sent the men running for the shaft. On December 31 operations had to be suspended.

The contractors proposed abandoning the heading entirely and driving the shaft deeper in an effort to hit a level of solid rock that would reach across the river. But since the soft fissure seemed to run vertically, Jacobs determined instead to bring in compressed air and continue the present heading. As the depth on the Manhattan side reached 120 feet below mean high water, and on the Ravenswood (Long Island) side 127 feet, a theoretical pressure of more than fifty pounds above atmospheric was needed—far beyond anything tunnel workers had ever endured. The hazards were real not only for the workmen, but on a less human and more crass level, for the contractors. McLaughlin and Reilly sought fresh guarantees and fees; Jacobs advised the gas company to refuse, and when the contractors went to court Jacobs undertook to drive the tunnel himself.

During the winter, a bulkhead with an air-lock and compressors was built forty feet behind the abandoned working face. Work was recommenced in February, with a pressure of thirty-five pounds per square inch. This was soon raised to thirty-seven to cope with water which continued to flood in. The dreaded bends at once made their appearance. On March 4, foreman Edward Ferris collapsed and died within a half hour. Many other men had to be rushed back into the air-lock after losing consciousness or suffering agony on their way home. Shifts were cut to an hour and a half, with an hour off before the next shift. Two more deaths occurred during the next weeks, as the heading inched forward in the teeth of repeated water inrushes and air pressure reached forty-eight pounds per square inch. Excavation was being carried forward under a cylindrical steel roof, built of one-eighth-inch sheet steel supported by angle bars. At last on April 8 the last of the soft feldspar was passed and bricked up. There had actually been only twenty-nine feet of the soft material, but it had very nearly wrecked the whole enterprise.

Now air pressure was removed and drilling recommenced, but it was soon found that some pressure had to be maintained to keep out the water. The new rock, even though requiring blasting, was relatively soft, and had to be lined with cast-iron as well as brick. The portion of the tunnel already bricked showed signs of buckling, and had to be relined, the brick ripped out, cast-iron rings emplaced, grouting done with Portland cement, and the brick restored.

Meantime the Ravenswood (Long Island) shaft, sunk June-November 1892, had bored through 285 feet of gneiss by March 1893. At this point a massive seam of almost liquid chlorite, a greenish soft rock, was struck. After several attempts to work through this muck, the heading was abandoned, pumping discontinued and the whole shaft and tunnel allowed to flood.

In the summer of 1893 Wall Street was hit by a short but severe panic and depression which made money so tight the East River Tunnel had to suspend work on August 8. The order to resume came September 30, but the delay had permitted the influx of water to soften the ground in front of the Manhattan heading, and Jacobs now decided—somewhat tardily, it appears to hindsight—that the job demanded a shield. The shield design was entrusted to Walton Aims, Jacobs's chief aide for the compressed-air work; the men reentered the Manhattan heading on September 22, 1893, and on November 17 the shield was assembled inside the tunnel and the advance begun. The first operation was a ticklish one. A bulkhead had been constructed to protect the heading during the work stoppage. When it was blasted away the shield entered an area where soft black mud flowed like a *purée* at the top of the shield, but a solid shelf of hard rock blocked the bottom. This rock had to be drilled and blasted with dynamite while somehow holding the *purée* back at the top long enough to give the drillers and blasters room to work. For a time an actual connection with the river was formed, and watery mud turned to muddy water, flowing down into the tunnel and carrying boulders, old boots and shoes, brick and tinware, and what gratified the workmen more, numerous crabs and mussels.

The air pressure was again stepped up to a terrific forty-eight pounds. Much of it escaped overhead, but since the area required in front of the shield was small, it was found possible to hold back the river bottom enough to carry on.

Thus directly in front of the shield the soup-soft mud was held up, dripping, shifting, and bubbling, by an air pressure equivalent to the weight of a heavy man standing on one's hand. In this intense atmosphere two men with pneumatic hand drills bored holes in rock, and backed out through the shield door to give way to two others who planted the dynamite charges and retreated in turn; the shield door was closed, allowing only the electric wire to pass through, the whole crew fell back a distance into the heading, and the blast was fired. Then through the shield door passed the labourers to shovel the rock debris into buckets, pass it back onto the waiting car, the roof still held uncertainly in position by the compact mass of heavy air. The labourers pulling back, the shield door again closed, the hydraulic jacks were turned on and the shield shoved forward a couple of feet. The crew went off duty, decompressing slowly in the air-lock, their places already taken by the relief gang. Nearly always, after working at this pressure, one of the men would collapse after reaching the outside, or on his way home. Many men took to carrying cards, "I am a compressed-air worker—take me to the air-lock at 71st Street."

On December 13 the 1st of the rock shelf was blasted and the shield entered fully on black mud. The shield pushed steadily through; in February 1894, hard gneiss was hit once more, but this time filling the whole tunnel space. The shield was dismantled and drilling and blasting resumed.

Jacobs had considered using the same shield in the Ravenswood heading, but calculating the delay in moving and reassembling the shield against the cost of building a new one, he had ordered a second shield, which was lowered into the Ravenswood shaft in the same month, February 1894. The seam of green chlorite was negotiated by the shield in a single month, and solid rock struck again. From here on it was regular drilling and blasting, without air pressure, and with bonuses to foremen to speed the work. In a week in June, 196 feet of tunnel were driven from the two headings. In July the headings met, despite all the difficulties and hazards, only two years from the beginning. The direction and gradient calculations were remarkably accurate; the headings coincided within one half inch in direction and an inch and a quarter in grade.

The East River Gas Tunnel is hardly one of New York's well-known tunnels today. Few New Yorkers are aware of its existence; yet its remarkably efficient execution played a decisive role in the history of modern New York. As Jacobs noted, the tunnel he had driven housed not only a three-foot gas main but a three-foot railway track, constructed to carry machinery into and debris out of the heading. Any time anyone wanted, Jacobs pointed out, an electric car could be installed to carry passengers from Long Island to Manhattan in two minutes. That lesson was one that could hardly be lost, though it took a few years to put it into effect.

The Thames Can Be Troublesome Too

E. W. Moir, back in England from his brilliant though unfinished stint under the Hudson, was commissioned to drive two tunnels under the Thames at Blackwall, about a mile below Greenwich, where the river was a quarter mile wide. The total length of the tunnels would be 6,200 feet, and the river bottom was no longer the solid workable London clay but a soft and treacherous sand and gravel mixture. Moir employed the same basic means as he had used on the Hudson —the Greathead shield, cast-iron lining and air-lock built into a brick bulkhead. In addition he maintained a "hanging screen" a few hundred feet back of the shield. This was an idea suggested, interestingly enough, by Alfred Beach in his *Scientific American* of August 21, 1880. The screen covered the upper half of the heading, and contained an emergency door. In this position it did not interfere with the coming and going of crews and passing out of excavated material, yet it provided an excellent safety device. In case of a sudden blow flooding the tunnel, compressed air would be trapped between the water and the top of the heading, along the whole distance from the shield to the screen. Such floodings actually occurred twice during the tunnel's construction, and both times workmen escaped through the emergency lock in the screen.

Moir designed his own rams, capable of exerting 4,800 tons pressure, for advancing the shield, as well as a travelling gantry, or platform, forty feet long, mounted on rails, for removal of excavated material. As under the Hudson, the shield was simply pushed forward, with the shutter partly open—sometimes as little as seven inches by three, with a resultant steady stream of silt pouring inward. Two air-locks were built into the bulkhead, one for the men, one for the material. Great care was taken to keep the air "pure," that is to keep the proportion of carbon dioxide low. It was to this that Moir attributed the Blackwall's relative freedom from "caisson disease"; actually, it had no bearing, although of course, excessive carbon dioxide itself is harmful.

The London County Council had laid down strict rules on ventilation, use of the air-lock, etc., and had obtained Parliamentary powers to compensate injured men. Most of its rules were of no real therapeutic value: hot coffee, drying rooms, etc. On the other hand, the Council's insistence on eight-hour shifts as in America, instead of the ten-and-a-half-hour shifts of the City and South London work, and the forty-five minute break given near the middle of the shift were definitely helpful. But most important of the precautions taken was certainly that of keeping the tunnel close to the river bottom—in some places within five feet of it—so that the total hydrostatic head never exceeded eighty feet. At this depth the air pressure needed to maintain equilibrium would be only about thirty-two pounds above atmospheric pressure, and this only for a short time. As a result, no lives were lost, and only three men permanently disabled.

Another feature of Moir's tunnelling at Blackwall was the use of electric lights, strung into the heading, a vast improvement over the smoking kerosene lamps of the old days.

The Blackwall tunnels were both finished by 1879. Two years later still another tunnel was driven under the Thames, at Greenwich, closer to the city, to connect the Isle of Dogs, Poplar, on the north bank, with Greenwich on the south. Once more compressed air had to be used, and once more it proved safe and effective, in combination with the shield.

This impressive array of successes by the Greathead method was continued into the new century—most notably in New York, where at long last the tunnel DeWitt Haskins had so boldly begun was about to be pushed to a finish.

CHAPTER TWELVE

New York Masters Its Rivers

Frank Davidson and Cyril Means, whose English Channel Tunnel idea started this book, have a famous precedent for turning from law books to tunnelling. Georgia-born William Gibbs McAdoo was one of the most prominent lawyers in New York at the turn of the century. Charles Jacobs's spectacular success under the East River started McAdoo wondering why the Hudson Tube scheme should not be revived. After conferring with Jacobs he felt even more certain the enterprise was feasible. McAdoo organized the New York and New Jersey Railroad Company and hired Jacobs as chief engineer. The object of the new company was not to produce tunnels for sale or lease to the big railroads, which had been Haskins's scheme, but rather to operate an independent suburban line. There were a number of questions in connection with such a line, but the important thing was to hole through the Haskins-Moir tunnel, which had been carried to 1,600 feet from the Manhattan heading.

Jacobs, who had himself worked on the tunnel under Moir, called together the most experienced compressed-air tunnelling team ever yet assembled—engineers, foremen, shield men, drillers, blasters, veterans of the East River Gas Tunnel, and some, like Jacobs himself, veterans of the Hudson twelve years earlier.

Moir, who had suspended work in full career because of the money shortage, had taken pains to leave the shield and other machinery in as secure condition as possible. Jacobs succeeded in recovering the Moir shield with little difficulty from the flooded tunnel, found it in first-rate condition and in a few weeks pushed it through to solid rock. The rock in most places blocked only the bottom of the shield, but for East River veterans, the problem was slight here, for the Hudson clay, compared with the decomposed rock of the East River, held magnificently. Besides, a new trick had been developed. The clay was dug away, upper segments of lining put in and held up by timbering—rough wooden beams and supports, braced against the leading edge of the brick lining. The rock was drilled shallow, and blown away a bit at a time.

When the rock gave way to soft silt some trouble was experienced in hold back the wet stuff long enough to erect the cast-iron lining, which consisted of nine-segment rings, each segment weighing 1,200 pounds, plus a key. Jacobs records in his history of the operation that at this point he armed his front line with blowtorches, with which the wet clay was baked hard—the first time anyone ever made bricks inside a tunnel heading, Jacobs notes. This story has been repeated several times, but modern engineers are sceptical. There is, in fact, a grapevine tradition somewhat unflattering to Jacobs. This report has it that the chief engineer entered the heading on an inspection and found some men busy at the shield with a blowtorch. What they were doing was actually straightening out a bend caused by careless shoving, but when the boss asked what was going on the ready-witted culprits explained that they were baking the clay face to facilitate excavation.

After 505 days' work, at an average advance of a trifle over three feet a day, Jacobs's men hit the target, the short twenty-year-old heading DeWitt Haskins had begun from Morton Street in Manhattan. The old bulkhead of that heading was broken through on March 11, 1904, thirty years after Haskins sank the original shaft in Jersey City. McAdoo was the first man to walk through. This tunnel was known for years after as "the McAdoo tunnel," and its successful completion gave impetus to McAdoo's political career, which eventually led to his appointment as Secretary of the Treasury in Woodrow Wilson's cabinet (1913-18) and a near miss at the Democratic Presidential nomination in 1924.

The decision to operate a suburban rail line had some far-reaching consequences. First of all it enabled Jacobs to reduce the diameter of the companion tunnel which was commenced immediately on completion of the McAdoo, at a considerable financial saving. The same reduction in diameter and consequent savings were made a little later when the second (downtown) pair of tubes were constructed. But the result was a narrow-gauge (three-foot) track, carrying a train that performed adequately for 1910 traffic, but was outdated within a generation.

The Downtown tubes (Church Street, Manhattan) ran into a single serious mishap in construction. The mud being uniformly soft, Jacobs gave orders to keep the shutter closed as the shield was advanced—to "shove blind." A night superintendent, dissatisfied with the speed of the work, opened the shutter. A jet of silt came shooting through with such force as to bury one workman and drive the others pell-mell to the air-lock, flooding the tunnel.

Recovery of the shield called for an ingenious new improvisation. Jacobs's first move—after firing the night superintendent—was to have a huge double fold of canvas, weighted at the edges, carried into the river on a scow and sunk directly over the point where the shield stood buried. Then a valve was opened in the air-lock, creating a partial vacuum and drawing a strong jet of mud from the flooded section into the completed section, whence it was taken out by the car-load. As the mud flowed through the air-lock, more entered the heading through the still-open shutter of the shield. Finally, after an enormous volume of silt had been carted from the tunnel, the river bottom overhead became depressed, carrying the canvas down over the shield, plugging the shutter. Now thousands of bags of clay were carried into the river and dumped into the hole, covering the canvas; meantime the heading was cleared, the shield recovered and the shutter closed. From this point on the shield made swift progress, driving 346 feet in one week, and once making seventy feet in a single twenty-four hour period—compared with Haskins's five feet a day in 1880.

The uptown tunnels were opened to 19th Street and Sixth Avenue in February 1908, and carried north to 33rd Street by November 1910. The downtown tunnels were opened from Church Street to the Pennsylvania Station in Jersey City and successive portions of the line put in operation during 1909 and 1910.

The westbound uptown tunnel, from the Hudson under Christopher Street to 12th Street and Sixth Avenue, a distance of nearly a mile, was driven largely through "New York rock," requiring a total of no fewer than 26,000 sticks of dynamite *en route*. Jacobs's men did the blasting expertly; not a single street surface or building was disturbed.

The Hudson Tubes are notable for a peculiarly intricate set of junctions on the Jersey side, a wrap-around arrangement executed in order to avoid intersections where the east- and westbound trains alternately run north to Jersey City and South to Newark and Hoboken (see picture).

If you ride the Hudson Manhattan Tubes today you will not be conscious of the difference in tunnel bore between the northernmost of the four (the westbound uptown) and the others, because after completion the big tube was lined with concrete to reduce its diameter to that of the others. But that northernmost tube is the famous McAdoo tunnel. A third of the way across you are at the point where Charles Jacobs recovered Moir's shield and began the final drive. Another third of the way and you are where Moir began work, and where Sir Benjamin Baker and Haskins's nephew were nearly trapped by a faulty air-lock door. For the next several hundred feet you are in the part of the tunnel which John Anderson drove with his pilot heading. A few moments before you reach the turn-off, where your train rises or descends, depending on whether you are going to Newark or Jersey City, you pass the point where Peter Woodland stood helpless with his men as the mud closed in. And at the junction point you are directly under the "homeopathic air-lock" where so many hundreds of men, racked by the bends, were rushed from all over the city. It takes only a few minutes to traverse the tunnel that took thirty years to build.

A New Tunnelling Trick: "Build and Sink"

As the long and painful story of the Hudson Tubes drew to a close, a wholly new method of under-river tunnelling was coming into being in Detroit, where the Michigan Central Railroad needed a tunnel under the Detroit River. This method was not really tunnelling at all, but it was cheap and perfectly successful. A trench was dredged in the river-bed, sections of double-tube steel tunnel were floated out and sunk into position, and the sections locked together. The technique was made possible by improved steel-casting. Its limitation was that it could not be done very well in deeper rivers. It was used with success in the Harlem River in New York and in many others places, but never in the Hudson. We will meet the "build-and-sink" method later in a very surprising place.

But in New York, the shield and compressed air remained king and queen of underwater tunnelling.

The Subway under the East River

The lesson of the East River Gas Tunnel was not lost on the men already busy constructing New York's enormous maze of subways. The new Brooklyn-Manhattan Transit Company began a tunnel in 1903, while Jacobs was still at work in the McAdoo tunnel. The BMT tunnel was dual, like the Hudson and Manhattan's, but with a larger diameter—fifteen feet, five and a half inches inside the flanges. The distance under river, from South Ferry to Montague Street, was 6,790 feet, about a mile and a quarter, and compressed air was used most of the way. Both tunnels were driven at once, from both headings, and on the Brooklyn side four shields were assembled in the two shafts, in order to dig the subway into Brooklyn at the same time as the tunnel under the river.

In the middle of the river quicksand was encountered, causing some serious difficulty for the tunnellers, and a newspaper scare for the public. There was some reason for raising the question, as the New York papers did, of whether a tunnel through quicksand could be maintained; in places the cast-iron rings were bent out of shape and the tunnel had to be reconstructed from within by further bracing to push up the roof, or, what was more easily done, by pushing down the floor.

Again an ingenious solution was found: concrete piles were sunk to depths of five to seventy-five feet, to hard material; the cast-iron tunnel was then solidly supported from below.

In the course of the controversy over the security of the tunnel, it was pointed out that many New York buildings stood on quicksand, and that quicksand, when confined, is perfectly capable of sustaining heavy weights.

The Man Who Blew out of a Tunnel

This BMT East River Tunnel is forever immortalized in the annals of tunnelling by a bizarre accident that occurred during its construction. One day in 1905 Richard Creegan, a veteran tunneller and foreman of an eight-man gang, was pushing the heading seventy-five feet under the river at a point where the tunnel line had only five feet of mud between it and the fifteen-foot-deep water. Suddenly a blow began just in front of the

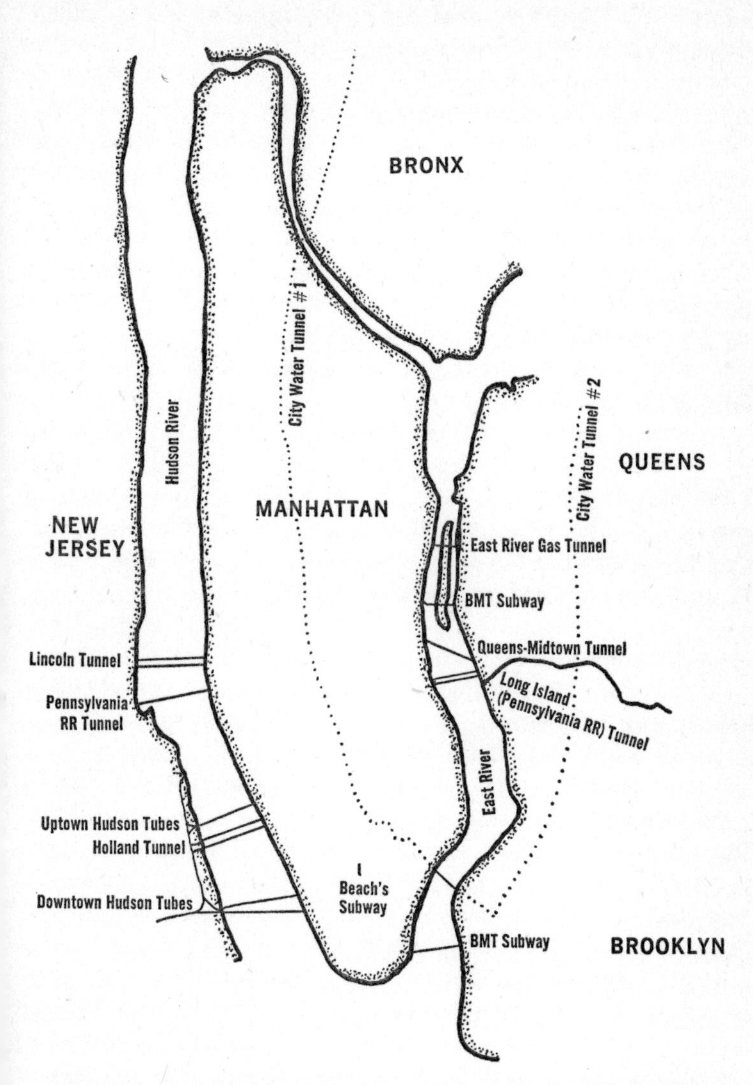

SOME OF NEW YORK'S FAMOUS UNDER-RIVER TUNNELS: Uptown Hudson Tubes include the McAdoo tunnel, which took thirty-four years to finish. BMT crossing of East River, lower Manhattan, is where a sandhog was blown clear through the tunnel and up into the river. City water tunnels run at depths of hundreds of feet in rock.

shield. Creegan, who had been on the lookout for such an emergency, seized a bag of hay ready at hand and hurled it at the hole. The bag was drawn straight to the opening by the escaping air, but disappeared from sight. Creegan grabbed a second bag, but as he lifted it, he himself was lifted bodily by the torrent of air. To the horror of the other men in front of the shield, the foreman was sucked into the blowhole. For a few seconds his body stuck in place, halting the escaping air, his legs dangling in the tunnel, his head and shoulders lost in the black mud above. Then in the rapid thrust and counter-thrust of compressed air and water Creegan's whole body was drawn upward, out of sight, as the remaining men tumbled through the shield door to safety.

Above, the eyes of longshoremen on the docks were drawn to the big bubbles signalling a blow in the tunnel below. Then suddenly to their utter amazement a tremendous column of water shot up, carrying with it a man, overalled, hip-booted, covered with mud but very much alive. In a very few minutes Creegan was rescued, completely unhurt.

Pennsylvania Railroad Tunnels under the North River

When the Pennsylvania Railroad decided to run its trains all the way into New York, voices were raised in apprehensive predictions. A tunnel in soft mud might sink after its completion, might it not? Jacobs, chief engineer of the project, considered sinking piles, as in the East River Subway tunnel, but the stability of the completed McAdoo tunnel soon made it evident no such underpinning was needed. An investigation was begun, however, into the possible movements of the tubes in the river mud, and eventually some rather interesting discoveries were made: the tubes rose and fell an eighth of an inch with the tide; they rose and fell about a quarter of an inch respectively each summer and winter; and over a period of years they slowly sank by a diminishing degree of settlement until the motion became negligible.

Long Island Railroad Tunnels

Shortly after, the Pennsylvania decided to tunnel under the East River to connect its subsidiary, the Long Island Railroad, with the new Pennsylvania Station on Manhattan which was opened in 1910. The very first of the four tunnels ran straight into quicksand. The best technique found for dealing with this treacherous material was to increase the air pressure to slightly above the hydrostatic head. This pushed the water back a little distance in the sand, leaving the material dryer and less fluid directly in front of the shield.

There was a danger, though. The air pressure inside the heading was constant from top to bottom, but the hydrostatic head (weight of water) increased towards the bottom, because of the greater depth. Thus more air pressure was needed at the bottom than at the top of the working face; yet how could you have two different air pressures in the same tunnel? The solution was to use enough air pressure to hold back the water at the bottom, and to provide extra cover at the top against the threatened blows. Scows moved out loaded with bags of clay; altogether some 300,000 cubic yards of clay was dumped in the river. It all had to be recovered afterward, to clear the channel to normal depth for navigation.

Blows of course did take place, and often; but each time the action of the well-disciplined gangs inside and the alertness of the scows above prevented disaster. Even when loss of air pressure reached 40,000 to 50,000 cubic feet a minute, the sandhogs stood their ground and flung bundles of hay or bags of clay into the holes, while emergency calls brought stepped-up pressure from the powerful compressing plants, and swift dumpings from the scows.

The Long Island Railroad tunnels mark a real turning point in tunnelling history. After this work, no river could seriously resist the array of weapons engineers could bring to bear against it: the big shield, the hydraulic jacks, the air-locks, the iron rings, the Portland cement grouting, the percussion drills, the well-controlled explosions, the high-powered air compressors.

Unfortunately, there were still the bends. Moir was justly proud of his homeopathic air-lock, and Jacobs expressed his satisfaction over the figures for the McAdoo work—of 29,000 men passed by the medical staffs for work under pressure above twenty pounds, there were only three fatalities recorded. There were, it was true, 1,573 cases requiring treatment in the air-lock—one case per foot of under-river tunnelling.

In the Long Island Railroad tunnels under the East River, there were 3,692 cases of bends recorded, and twenty deaths.

Of course the number of workers was much higher than in the McAdoo stage of the Hudson Tube. Still, the figures were grim.

A set of rules was formulated by Dr. Andrew H. Smith, chief surgeon of the McAdoo, and the man who had originally suggested the homeopathic air-lock in 1873. These rules were posted for the men:

1. Never enter the air-lock with an empty stomach.
2. Use as far as possible a meat diet, and take warm coffee freely.
3. Always put on extra clothing on coming out, and avoid exposure to cold.
4. Exercise as little as may be during the first hour after coming out, and lie down if possible.
5. Use intoxicating liquors sparingly. Better not at all.
6. Take at least eight hours sleep every night.
7. See that the bowels are open every day.
8. Never enter the air-lock if at all sick.
9. In exit from the air-lock, the time occupied is to be: five minutes for each atmosphere above normal.

These rules indicate less an understanding of compressed-air sickness than a fixation on the normal health regulations of the day. Only in his last rule did Dr. Smith touch the real question, and there with an appalling inadequacy. The minimum rate of decompression actually considered safe today is twenty minutes per atmosphere of pressure—four times Dr. Smith's recommendation. One cannot escape the suspicion that Dr. Smith's employers did not show much enthusiasm for slow decompression for their men. At forty-five pounds pressure, this meant a full hour's decompression; or a full hour's pay without work.

The other condition of overriding importance, the time spent under pressure, was also given only perfunctory consideration, though Charles Jacobs reduced working hours for men under the "highest pressure," i.e., forty-five to forty-nine pounds per square inch, to an hour and a half at a time, with one hour rest between, an arrangement that probably struck Jacobs's employers as extraordinarily liberal.

It was noted during the Long Island Railroad work that 86 per cent of the cases of bends occurred during the first hour after decompression. Efforts were made to induce the men to stay near the air-lock for an hour after finishing work, instead of going straight home, but without much success, since no one wished to suggest an hour's pay for the hour's wait. The sandhogs of that day had no union.

Medical science of course had a very insufficient comprehension of compressed-air sickness. Contrary to what Dr. Smith imagined, the real villain in the air is not carbon dioxide but nitrogen, the gas which makes up most of the atmosphere. When a man in compressed air breathes, more nitrogen is dissolved in the body fluids and tissues than under normal pressure. When he returns to normal pressure, some of this gas is liberated, especially from the blood plasma and body fat. If this liberation comes too suddenly, the nitrogen forms bubbles that block the small blood vessels. Bubbles may also form in fatty materials—myelin sheaths, bone marrow, adrenal cortex and subcutaneous tissue, leading to numerous, unpredictable, painful disorders.

French physiologist Paul Bert made the basic discovery—air embolism—back in 1878; but it was a long time before embolism was connected with the bends. Yet, as is evident from Dr. Smith's prescription of the air-lock for treatment, and his rule for slow decompression—even if hardly slow enough—doctors did have a glimmering of the real trouble.

In the end politicians had to do what doctors and contractors did not—enforce serious measures. The New York State Legislature passed a set of regulations on compressed-air work, and while some of them still were completely beside the point, a crucial area was hit hard. A table was drawn up regulating precisely the length of time a man could spend under various degrees of pressure. The highest pressure permitted was from forty-five to forty-nine pounds, in which a worker was allowed to remain only forty-five minutes at a time, with only two such shifts a day, separated by a four-hour interval.

In the BMT subway tunnels driven soon after, the dramatic effect of the new regulations appeared. Despite working pressures of up to forty-eight pounds, and despite twice as many decompressions as for the Long Island Railroad tunnels, the BMT recorded only 680 cases and two deaths—a fifth as many cases and a tenth as many fatalities.

But even today, every sandhog who works under pressure carries a badge identifying him as a compressed-air worker and reading, *If ill, rush by ambulance to* (designated) *air-lock.*

CHAPTER THIRTEEN

The Drama of the Simplon

In the whole history of tunnelling, one tunnel stands out above all others for greatness of conception, foresight in planning, and resourcefulness in execution, in the face of stunning and unexpected blows of fate. This is the mighty Simplon, twelve and a half miles long, to this day the longest transportation tunnel in existence. Thousands of Europeans and Americans ride through it every day on such luxury trains as the famous Simplon-Orient Express, with no thought of the struggle that made possible their swift and pleasant journey.

We left Alpine tunnelling with the completion of the tragedy-ridden St. Gothard, connecting Switzerland and Italy. The harsh lessons of Gothard were taken to heart by contractors and engineers, and subsequent Alpine tunnelling gave careful attention to ventilation and hygiene, as well as organization of crews, techniques of removing debris, heading systems, and drilling. Expanding trade and railway growth dictated another Alpine north-south tunnel, and the Simplon Pass was the natural site. A tunnel under it had been suggested as early as 1853, but the size of the Monte Leone massif gave even the most daring engineers pause. Several plans were put forward involving ascents on either side by loop tunnels winding in and out of the mountain, with a relatively short main tunnel near the top. Such a design would make an almost prohibitively expensive operation, and after the completion of Mont-Cenis and commencement of Gothard, bolder projects were brought forward, calling for a long, deep main tunnel. In 1875 Louis Favre was consulted, and suggested a route from Brig in Switzerland to Iselle in Piedmont, north-west to south-east, a distance of just under twenty kilometres (over twelve miles), passing through Monte Leone at an altitude of only 700 metres. This daring scheme provoked lengthy debate. Could a tunnel at such a depth, well over a mile at the deepest point sustain the enormous rock pressures? And could any means be found to ventilate a heading where the depth promised temperatures of well over a hundred degrees Fahrenheit? A tunnel, open at both ends, is one thing; a heading, a horizontal shaft pushed deep into a mountain, quite another. Under Mont-Cenis the geothermal degree had proved to be 58.4 metres; that is, for every 58.4 metres of depth the rock temperature rose one degree Centigrade. This "high" geothermal degree meant a moderate temperature inside the headings. The St. Gothard geothermal degree was forty-seven metres, making the temperature of the headings, which lay at about the same elevation as the Mont-Cenis, correspondingly higher. The Simplon route designated by Favre ran 2,150 metres—a mile and a quarter—under the peak, 500 metres deeper than Mont-Cenis. Even if the geothermal degree proved high—and there was not particular reason to anticipate that it would be—the temperatures would soar above 40° C, which is over 100° F. Furthermore, there were complicating geological factors which might well heat the rock up even more. A reasonable guess for the Simplon's deepest point might very well be 120° F.

While the Simplon continued to baffle the engineers, several other rail tunnels were driven in various part of the Alps. The seven-mile Arlberg, between Austria and Switzerland, reached a depth of only 720 metres, less than half of what the Simplon would be, but its exceptionally easy—and therefore profitable—completion, in less than four years, made a sensation. The rate of advance was better than double that of the Gothard. The Ferroux drill, already proven at Gothard, was highly effective, but even more dramatic was the success of a newer drill, the Brandt, designed on an entirely novel principle. Unlike all the previous rock drills of Europe and America, the Brandt did not depend on speed of rotation for its penetrating power; it turned at a lazy eight to ten rotations per minute, but was backed by a water pressure from its hydraulic jack of ten to twelve tons. Of bigger gauge than previous drills, it produced a perforation a yard deep and three and a half inches in diameter, large enough to accommodate a five-pound stick of dynamite. With charges this size, only a dozen holes were necessary in the rock face, compared with seventy or eighty back in the black-powder days of Mont-Cenis. Drilling time was from twelve to twenty-five minutes. In addition, water under pressure was delivered to the drill hole simultaneously with the boring, thus saving time in the essential operation of cooling the drill holes before planting the dynamite charges.

The inventor of this excellent tool was a German engineer named Alfred Brandt. From 1883 on, the Brandt drill became the foremost Alpine tunnelling tool. Yet the Brandt drill alone could not overcome the difficulties of tunnelling the Simplon Pass. The basic problem remained: How to keep a heading cool enough to work when it ran a mile beneath a mountain?

The Brandt drill could not solve the problem, but its inventor could. Alfred Brandt proposed to the Jura-Simplon Railway an entirely new method of tunnel construction. Instead of a single-tube, double-track tunnel, said Brandt, let us build two separate single-track tunnels.

The beauty of this revolutionary concept cannot be appreciated at a glance. The first reaction of a government official or railway director was probably that it would double the cost. Actually, Brandt's plan realized a reduction in costs, but this was secondary to the main point, which was that it was the only plan which made tunnelling the Simplon possible.

Side by side, Brandt would drive two advance headings into the mountain, as bottom galleries of the twin tubes. Every two hundred metres the two headings would be connected by cross-hatches. Powerful ventilating equipment, installed at the mouth of Gallery II, would blow air down this gallery, through the appropriate cross-hatch into Gallery I, cool the air where the crew was working, and return out the portal of Gallery I.

This was only the most salient of several important advantages in Brandt's plan. The supply of materials—dynamite, drills, lining materials, timbering, etc.—was greatly facilitated; likewise, removal of debris; the little narrow-gauge trains could, by backing and filling, run on an efficient circular route, like the ventilation. The train could enter Gallery II loaded with materials, follow the cross-hatch into Gallery I, unload materials, load debris, and back out of Gallery I without interfering with the next train coming in Gallery II.

Still another advantage was that the indispensable drainage canal could be dug in Gallery II, so that the water outflow would not interfere with the operations of the finishing crew in Gallery I.

The directors of the Jura-Simplon Railway, impressed with

Brandt's reasoning as well as his reputation, signed a contract with Brand, Brandau and Co. on September 20, 1893, to construct Simplon I with the advance gallery of Simplon II for a total cost of 69,500,000 francs, in a space of five and a half years. The Swiss Government ratified the plan in July 1894. The Italian Government ratified in turn, and a treaty was signed in December 1896. Financial arrangements, by which the two governments and the local cantons contributed to the cost, were not completed till the summer of 1898, and in the fall of that year Brandt began assembling his base depots at Iselle and Brig. Spur lines were built, narrow-gauge locomotives and cars brought in, barracks, repair shops, etc., went up, dynamite, drills, compressed-air equipment and all the rest began pouring in.

Besides the Brandt drill, there were some notable minor improvements in technique. Immediately after firing a blast, a dozen jets of water were directed against the face. This water was kept cold even after the heading had advanced deep into the mountain by packing the water pipe with charcoal. The cooling, together with the ventilation, reduced delay between attacks by permitting the mucking crew to approach at once.

An explosive gelatin, more powerful than dynmite, was used in the Swiss heading, where the rock was softer, except for occasional quartz, dolomite, and gypsum. The gelatin contained the very high ratio of 83 per cent nitro-glycerine. At the Italian end, where the work was almost entirely in hard geniss, conventional dynamite was used, 64 per cent nitro.

Experimentation with two novel techniques proved them unsatisfactory: shooting a jet of water at the face simultaneously with the detonation, and using liquid air as an explosive. The former made no appreciable difference in the speed of cooling, and the latter proved hazardous.

Work began November 13, 1898. A little over a year later Brandt died, giving the three great Alpine tunnels a grim record; Sommeiller had died before the completion of Mont-Cenis, Favre had been felled by a heart attack midway through Gothard.

At the time of Brandt's death the headings were making good progress, and though the temperatures of the rock (in the 60s, Fahrenheit) gave cause for some uneasiness about the future, no difficulties had yet arisen.

It was not till 1901, when more than two years of efficient drilling and blasting had carried the twin headings forward a total distance of some 5,000 metres out of a total of 19,825, that heat became a serious problem. Rock temperatures reached nearly 90° F. While engineers debated this problem, another intruded without ceremony. On October 1, in the

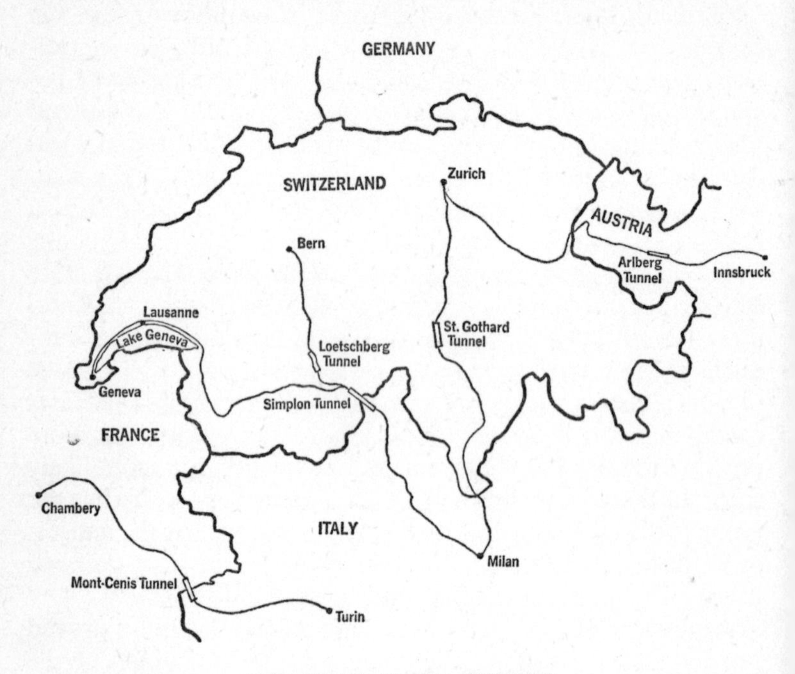

THE GREAT ALPINE TUNNELS

south heading, the drill suddenly produced a spurt of water that rose to the rate of 8,100 gallons a minute, more than double the volume that had disrupted work on the St. Gothard in 1873-74. Brandt had placed his drainage canal in Gallery II, out of the way of the finishing workers, but the torrent of water far exceeded the canal's capacity; both galleries were turned into mountain streams. In three weeks the inrush increased to an incredible 12,000 gallons a minute. Enough water was entering the heading to supply Switzerland's largest city, Zurich, with a generous daily water supply of one hundred gallons per person.

The flood put a total halt to work; engineers, foremen, and

labourers simply stood back and marvelled at the river that was pouring out of their tunnel. Presently the torrent diminished enough to allow the men to return to work, when they found that the water had had at least one beneficial effect; its temperature, in the low 60s Fahrenheit, had helped hold down the threatening temperature of the air in the heading.

A month later, the water returned in enormous force. On December 5, it was pouring into the south heading at the fantastic rate of 13,800 gallons a minute—and now the water began warming up. From the 60s it passed into 70s and 80s and finally went over 90° F. The heading had hit nothing less than an underground river, and the flow continued week after week, months on end. In the spring of 1902 it diminished a little—to 10,740 gallons a minute.

The deeper the headings bored into the mountain, the more serious became another difficulty—rock swellings. A mountain is essentially an enormous pile of boulders, some hundreds of thousands of metres in dimensions, some mere gravel or sand. When a tunnel is driven into the pile, various shiftings occur, and the bigger the mass above the tunnel, the more pressure there is from above and consequently the more likely such shifts become. Once the tunnel is walled, assuming the lining is thick enough and hard enough, it is secure; the danger, as we have seen in the St. Gothard, comes in the stage between driving the advance heading and completing the lining.

Again Brandt's foresight in driving parallel headings proved providential, for this system facilitated the completion of the lining in the shortest possible time. Nonetheless, cave-ins threatened constantly and sometimes occurred, though never catastrophically.

The north heading pushed ahead through constantly rising temperatures. In the spring of 1902 the heat went over 50° C. (122° F.). In July it hit a broiling 52.80 (125° F.).

The heading was 7,461 metres from the portal—still 2,500 metres from the midpoint. But due to the profile of the mountain, the north heading had to pass under the peak before reaching midpoint. For the next 2,000 metres, working in short shifts, the men pushed on through rock whose temperature never dropped below 120° F. The Austrian geologist's guess had proven highly inaccurate. The Simplon geothermal degree was actually thirty-seven metres. Rock fragments from the blasting were too hot to pick up. Brandt's ingenious ventilation system was taxed to the utmost—and once again his far-sighted two-gallery plan saved the day. A single gallery would have been absolutely impossible to ventilate at this temperature.

Through 1902 and 1903, in constant terrific heat and with frequent water inrushed, the work was relentlessly pushed on. In June 1904, a new major influx came at a temperature of 138° F. The heading had driven straight into a hot spring. Men were scalded before they could flee down the gallery.

Yet the work was pressed on. It was suspended, renewed, suspended again, as the rock temperature rose higher and higher. Finally the rock walls reached an incredible, and unbearable, 131° F. (55 C.). No man could stand such heat. The crew was pulled back. At this point the north heading had actually passed the summit of the mountain; the temperature would doubtless decline from here on. However, it was simply impossible to continue to work in such heat, and the decision was made to withdraw the whole crew from the north heading and finish from the south.

Eight months later, on February 24, 1905, the south crew blasted through the main gallery. On July 6, Galley II was holed through. Completion of the main tunnel was accomplished in a few months, and on June 1, 1906, the first train entered.

As American engineer Charles W. Comstock said that the Simplon broke all tunnelling records for speed "in the face of

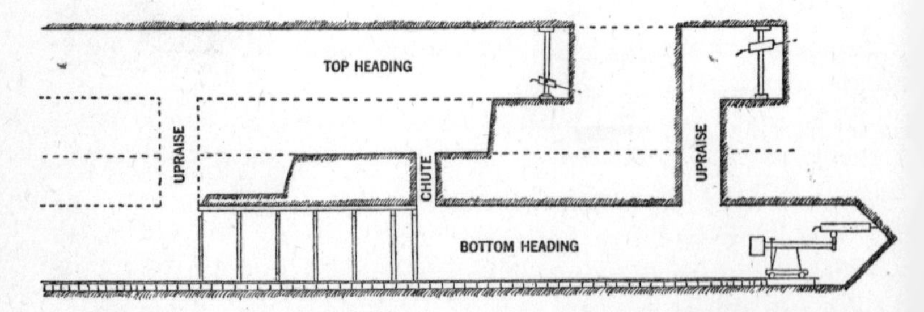

HOW THE ALPINE TUNNELS WERE DRIVEN: Longitudinal section of the Loetschberg shows the advance heading at bottom, the upraises (vertical shafts), the top heading, which was driven by hand, the chute through which excavated material was dropped, and the timbering to hold up centre during final stage.

the most discouraging obstacles ever met underground or on the surface." The average advance for both headings, including stoppages, was 130 metres per month, equal to the best speed achieved at Gothard, and far exceeding the Gothard average. Considering the totally unexpected difficulties with which the engineers laboured, the rate was remarkable; nonetheless, the engineering firm had to pay a forfeit. During the construction, in October 1903, a new contract had been drawn up taking some account of the unforeseen obstacles. The total price was raised to 76,263,000 francs, and the termination date moved ahead to April 30, 1905. Even this date could not be met, due to the necessity of stopping work completely in the north heading in mid-1904.

Brandt had died early in the progress of the work. Before the Simplon was finished, three of his original partners also succumbed. The mortality rate among these Alpine engineers suggests a considerable degree of strain.

The Loetschberg: Mountain Treachery

Two important tasks remained to complete the essential rail links through the Swiss Alps—Simplon II, which would bring the great new tunnel to full double-track capacity, and a tunnel through the Bernese Oberland to the north, connecting the Simplon-Rhone Valley route with Bern and the Rhine Valley. Of two alternate tunnel routes, the safer lay through the Wildstrubel massif, forty kilometres west of the Simplon, but local interests led to the choice of the Loetschberg route, in the valley of the Kander River. The main tunnel here would pierce 14,536 metres of mountain, about eight and a half miles, with a maximum depth of 1,570 metres—approximately the length of the St. Gothard, at a slightly lesser depth.

The Loetschberg crews improved the attack times of the Simplon to four hours, forty-three times, largely a result of new American Ingersoll-Rand drills. Both north and south headings were proceeding at this rapid rate in the summer of 1908, when the north heading entered the Gastern Valley, where it was to cross under the Kander River. The tunnel depth was 180 metres below the floor of the valley, and the geologists had reported the soft valley bed extended down 100 metres, giving 80 metres of solid rock cover. The contractors themselves were sceptical, but the scientists were persuasive, and work was pushed ahead. The limestone had recently given way to granite, a much harder material, so short drilling with heavy charges was the order of the day. On July 24 the attack crew was operating as usual. The Ingersoll-Rand drill perforated the rock face to the required depth and in the normal number of places and was pulled back along the narrow-gauge rail out of range of the blast. The dynamiters rammed their charges home, fused and plugged them, and withdrew to a safe distance. The detonation was set off.

The granite was blasted into a million fragments—and from beyond, without a moment's warning, a tremendous mass of sand, water, and gravel torrented into the heading, burying men and machinery almost before a cry could be uttered. The raging flood raced through the whole heading, not one of the twenty-five workmen in the attack crew escaped.

The geologists had made an appalling miscalculation. A cleft of sand extended down from the river to the incredible depth of three hundred metres. The last blast had shattered the thin curtain of granite that had separated the unsuspecting tunnellers from this frightful trap. It was the single worst disaster in the history of Alpine tunnelling.

So massive was the break in the river bottom, so complete

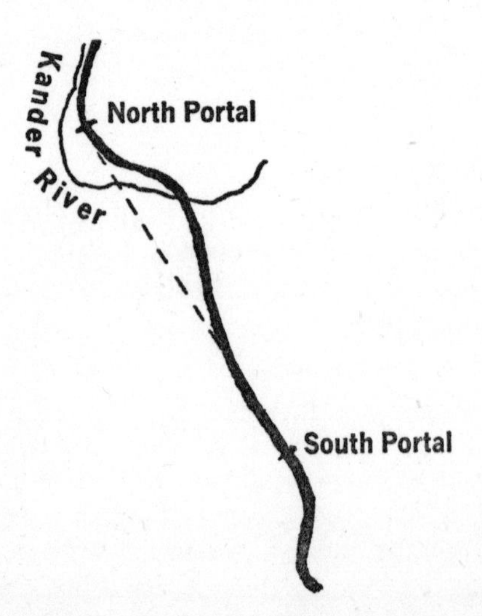

THE LOETSCHBERG DISASTER: Dotted line shows original tunnel route which led to disaster under Kander River.

the wreckage of the tunnel that the engineers finally decided to abandon nearly half the heading. The disaster had occurred at a point 2,675 metres from the north portal. At 1,425 metres from the portal, a tremendous bulwark, ten metres (thirty-three feet) thick was constructed, with drains to release accumulated water. A commission of engineers was convened to study the problem, and after considering draining the old tunnel and proceeding on its axis, or experimenting with the very new freezing process, the commission recommended the safe solution: to carry the heading upstream and cross the Kander at a more secure place. This was done, and a few months later the new heading pushed under the treacherous valley. Granite gave way to limestone as the heading probed forward under the river. Tense days and nights followed. Finally the attack once more hit granite. The heading was safely across the valley. The relieved engineers gave themselves a banquet.

Though numerous difficulties had to be overcome in completing the tunnel and in constructing loop approaches the rest of the work was anticlimatic.

Despite the terrific setback imposed by the disaster and the necessity for adding over 2,000 metres to the work, the Loetschberg was holed through in March 1911, and completed the following year ahead of schedule.

Simplon II—a Unique Tunnelling Job

Work on Simplon II was delayed from 1906 to 1912 by a lawsuit between the railway line and Brandt, Brandau over the original contract, whose terms were no longer realistic. In the end the Swiss Federal Railways appointed a special commission of its own to carry out the work. F. Rothpletz of Bern, a veteran of Simplon I, was made chief engineer.

The problem was to enlarge the gallery to full diameter in the most expeditious and safest way. The existing gallery was at the bottom of the diameter. Normally, the finishing crew would tunnel upward from this gallery in several places, then dig out a top gallery, shovelling the debris down onto loading cars below. Then the top side sections would be excavated, the middle sections, and finally the bottom side sections. But Rothpletz had his bottom heading completed, with no attack crew at work in it. Therefore, he reasoned, he could profitably launch a second attack by drilling and blasting, at the top of the diameter, producing a whole new heading, and providing two galleries for the finishing workers to operate from. This "strozzetto" was separated from the existing gallery by the coping, through which material was dropped into the cars standing below. From the strozzetto the whole "calotte"—the upper, domed section of the tunnel, could readily be excavated.

Since the existing gallery contained the drainage canal, which would be a permanent feature of the finished tunnel, Rothpletz decided to make it run not on the centre axis of the tunnel but as the outside half of the bottom section (Section 8 in drawing on page 88).

This system was used throughout, with an important modification for certain sections where the gallery passed through soft material and cave-ins were feared. The most dangerous stretch lay for some fifty metres at a point 4,500 metres from the south portal. Here serious cave-ins had threatened the construction of Simplon I, and it was feared that the blasting for Simplon II might bring fresh shiftings. Rothpletz took the unusual step of leading a special crew through Simplon I directly to this point, driving small shafts upward, blasting the gallery, widening the calotte, excavating the lower part of the tunnel, and completing it at once. Since Simplon I was lined for safety, Rothpletz employed the Belgian method. A portion of the roof lining was removed, short shafts were driven upward and the strozzetto driven. As this was widened into the calotte, it was constantly supported by timbering. When the calotte was completed and ready for lining, the roof of the lower gallery was again filled to protect it in case of a disaster in the upper chamber. Now the timbering was removed piece by piece as the lining was put in. The whole section was finished without trouble.

The lining material for this section and for other "*Druckpartien*" (pressure spots) was natural rock; for most of the tunnel, running through natural rock, lining was done with softer, more easily workable limestone.

Despite all the precautions, however, several dangerous cave-ins of Tunnel I occurred when blasting in Tunnel II caused a shifting of the mountain above. If a single large boulder was split, one half of the formation might "lean" heavily on Tunnel

I, breaking through a roof or wall previously perfectly secure. Again, single boulders in the thick wall between the two tunnels might be loosened by a blast and caused to topple towards one or the other gallery. Notably in the south heading, a little more than 3,000 metres from the Iselle portal, a series of cave-ins broke into the new work. With a noise like a cannon shot, a mass of rock would suddenly ram forward into the gallery. Or a rumble from above would signal an earthquake-like shock which caused the workers to drop tools and run for their lives. Or sometimes the wall between the two galleries received the shock and collapsed into Tunnel I. Where Tunnel II ran in solid rock, no difficulties of any sort were encountered.

In some especially dangerous places heavy iron frames, rectangular in form, were emplaced during construction rather than wooden timbering; and where future danger was anticipated, permanent iron rings, of the shape of the tunnel vault, similar to those used in under-river tunnelling, were installed. Cement grouting was forced behind the ironwork, just as in under-river work.

Despite the rock shiftings and cave-ins, the work was making excellent progress (better than ten metres a day) when a new kind of eruption struck—the European cataclysm of 1914. Switzerland remained neutral, but so many workmen and engineers were called to the colours that the work was brought virtually to a halt.

In 1919, with the war over and labour again abundant, the tunnel was resumed. Through 1920 and 1921 it was pushed steadily, and on December 4, 1921, the keystone was set at 11,592 metres from the north portal—well over half the distance having been covered from the Swiss heading.

Simplon II produced one disagreeable surprise—despite hygienic precautions regarded as exceptionally complete, the silicosis rate was high. The reason for it lay in the pneumatic drills. The men working on Simplon II, spread out along Gallery II, armed with this excellent tool, so familiar to modern city dwellers, frequently hit silicate rock where the hammer-drill created clouds of rock dust which settled in the workers' lungs. There is an irony here, for the solution, the use of water with the drill, had actually been applied—unwittingly —in the driving of the advance heading. The Brandt drill had been supplied with water, not as a silicosis preventive, but to cool the drill hole more quickly for the dynamite charge. In the hand-drilling, no such consideration arose.

But the casualty rate among Simplon workers could scarcely draw attention in a Europe in which men were falling by the millions on the battlefield, and indeed, the completion of Simplon II seems almost an ironic island of peaceful achievement in a half-decade of international destruction. The completion came twenty-three years after Alfred Brandt's opening blast at Brig in 1898, and forty-six years after Louis Favre's blueprint of the route through Monte Leone.

To this day the mighty pair of Simplon tunnels remain man's greatest single tunnelling achievement.

CHAPTER FOURTEEN

London Starts the Underground Rush

By far the busiest tunnelling operations in all history have been carried out under the cities of the Western world in the past hundred years. It was not quite a century ago that the world's first underground was opened in London. We have noted Peter Barlow's far-sighted proposals for underground transit. Actually Barlow's idea grew rather naturally out of a development already under way. In the 1840s when the railway boom was on in Britain, Greater London was bursting with a population of nearly two and half million. Bringing railway lines into the centre of the metropolis threatened serious disruption; yet to leave the terminals on the city's periphery was unthinkable. The intelligent, if obvious, solution hit on was to bring the lines in underground. With minimum disturbance of traffic, the streets could be trenched and covered, a section at a time.

The railways inside London, a second problem arose. Passengers from the north, heading for embarkation at Dover or Southampton, had to detrain at one station, take a cab, and get on another train at another station. For freight, the problem was even more acute. The City Solicitor, Charles Pearson, suggested extending the underground lines beneath Farringdon Street to connect the terminals. The plan was authorized by Parliament in 1856. In 1862 the first section was finished—the first underground city transit system in the world. The four-mile line was opened January 10, 1863, and was such a success from the start that a second line, the London District Railway, was opened between High Street, Kensington, and Gloucester Road in 1868, and the original known as the Metropolitan, extended. For the Thames crossing, a marvellous tunnel was already there: Brunel's, until now hardly used. During the 1880s the London underground continued to grow.

Up to this point all the work was done by cut-and-cover. But now, partly because further crossings of the Thames were needed, and partly out of a desire to avoid interfering with traffic, the shield method was adopted. Peter Barlow was no longer alive, but James Henry Greathead carried out the work, including the tunnel under the Thames which we have already described.

This underground had another important distinction; electric power for traction had just appeared on the scene, and the City and South London was the first to install it (December 1890).

Only one mistake was made in the construction of Greathead's tunnel; the diameter chosen was too small. This problem, of enlarging the tunnel bore to permit use of bigger underground coaches, was met in 1922 by an ingenious means. An "open" shield was designed through which trains could pass. A ring of cast-iron segments was removed, the shield jacked forward, and the ring replaced behind the shield with extra segments to enlarge it. Traffic was hardly interrupted.

Glasgow: Danger under the Clyde

The second city to undertake construction of railways was Glasgow, and the porous sand under the Scottish metropolis proved a far more formidable ground than had London's solid clay. One mishap followed another. The first two lines built were local suburban railways, passing underground as they entered the City. Steam locomotives were used, and in the tunnels the passengers almost suffocated. These two lines were built by cut-and-cover in the 1880s and '90s; the Glasgow District Underground, a shield-driven all-underground metropolitan railway, proposed in 1890, met with considerable opposition from the start. Four shields were assembled in a shaft in the heart of Glasgow in March 1891, two started towards the River Clyde, two in the opposite direction. The 410-foot river tunnel, predictably, was the hardest part of the job. Greathead had tunnelled under the Thames for the City and South London just four years earlier, and though two other rivers had been tunnelled by shield and compressed air—the Fidler's Ferry Aqueduct under the Mersey at Liverpool and the Sarnia-Port Huron tunnel under the St. Clair River—the method was still very new and had never been attempted in loose, sandy soil such as that under the Clyde.

Before the tunnellers had gone eighty feet under the river

they had experienced no fewer than ten serious blowouts, including one in which the entire timbering of the heading was blown up through the river, leaving an enormous hole in the river bottom and of course flooding the heading.

The contractor resigned the work, which was taken up by a more enterprising and more determined man, George Talbot. Talbot introduced several reforms, none of which amounted to a new tunnelling technique, but which were important adaptations of the Greathead method. Air pressure was increased and reduced with the changing tides. A vigilant check was kept on the river bottom and clay dumped whenever a weak spot was detected.

Down in the tunnel excavation was carried on in front of the shield for no more than the space occupied by one tunnel ring; the shield was then advanced and the ring emplaced. Finally, Talbot broke the Glasgow blue law by keeping his crews at work over Sunday, as well as on Saturdays, holidays, and through mealtimes. This continuous-shift operation involved the employment of more men, but it not only speeded the work, it made it safer. Pauses under such uncertain ground, especially the long weekend pause, were dangerous.

Success silenced Talbot's critics; the tunnel was completed under the river without a single additional serious blowout. The second tube was completed in three and a half months despite a terrifying accident. Halfway under the river fire broke out, burning with extraordinary intensity in the compressed air. Fifteen workers were cut off in the heading; though the fire itself could not reach them in the portion of finished tunnel where they were trapped, neither could they escape through the debris. And above all, the conflagration threatened their air supply.

In Chapter 12 we mentioned an invention of James Henry Greathead, following his construction of the Tower underground—the grouting pan. This device depended on compressed air to force the liquid cement into the annular space outside the lining. Under the River Clyde, the fifteen trapped tunnellers had the grouting pan. Ripping the compressed air hose loose, they took turns breathing from it, and despite the smoke that filled the heading, stayed alive.

Talbot meanwhile lost no time in beginning a desperate rescue operation. Leading a party into the parallel tube, he located the point opposite the trapped men. With crowbars and sledges, the iron plates were torn out. Now only five feet separated the rescuers from the rescued, but five feet of treacherous River Clyde sand. A hasty check of the river bottom was made, the air pressure in the heading regulated, and with pick and shovel the men drove into the sand. Timbers were shoved into place to reinforce; the gingerly but hurried advance was continued. Now the plates of the other tube were struck. Again, the crowbars and sledge hammers, only now they were plied from inside the tiny five-foot cross heading, with a destructive blow threatening every moment. After a terrific struggle, the plates were warped loose and battered in, and the fifteen exhausted men pulled to safety.

Talbot had still more troubles before finishing his job. At one point, not under the river, he hit an abandoned, water-filled quarry and a quarter of a mile of tunnel was flooded before the water could be halted. In another place an underground stream flooded one heading, which actually had to be bricked up, and the tunnel holed through from the opposite heading.

Even after the Glasgow District underground was finished, problems were not quite over. Its detractors to the contrary, the public loved it—in fact after its opening on January 21, 1897, under the uniform fare of one penny for an unlimited ride, it was found that numerous customers spent the whole day in the underground. A ticket system finally had to be adopted.

A notable feature of the Glasgow District underground was that it used the cable technique, not going over to electricity till 1935.

The Rush Is On

Budapest built its first subway in 1894-96, two miles long under Andrassy Street. In 1895 Boston began construction on the first American subway, under Washington, Tremont, and Boylston Streets. Most of the route was cut-and-cover construction, though a "roof shield," consisting of the upper part of an ordinary Beach shield, was used in some stretches. The subway went into operation, first with single cars, in 1898.

The Paris Métro, under consideration for many years, was finally authorized in 1898, and the original section, from the Porte de Maillot to the Porte de Vincennes under the Champs-Elysées and the Rue de Rivoli, completed by 1900 by a new

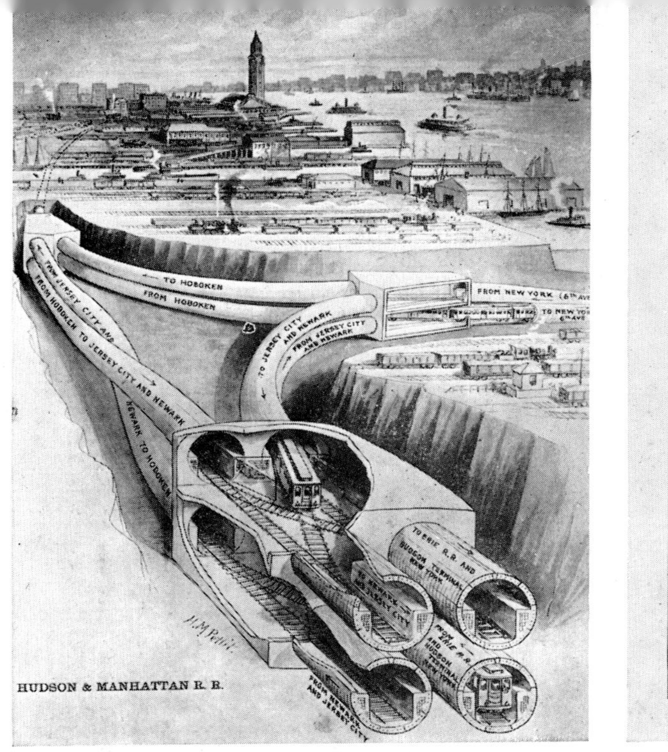

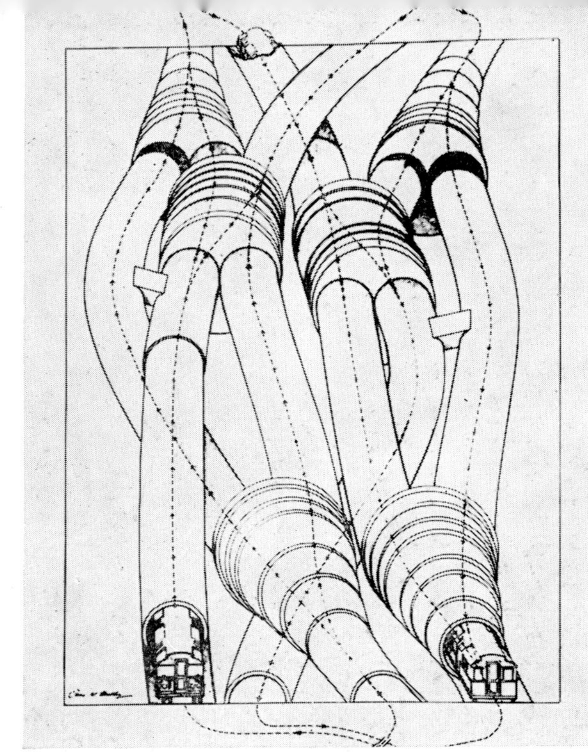

The underground railway systems of New York and London, as a result of the need to avoid track intersections, contain some most complex tunnel junctions. *(Left)* Cut-away picture of the Hudson Tubes entering New Jersey. *(Right)* Diagram of the Camden Town junction where four lines converge and separate again

(Above) The Moscow Metro, opened in May 1935, is still expanding. Though it is not as large as some underground systems, its construction has been planned with great thoroughness, anticipating future demands upon the city's transport services. A section of the Metro under construction near the centre of the city

(Left) Modern American tunnelling. A powerful erector lifts a giant block into place in construction of a Detroit factory water-tunnel

version of the cut-and-cover method. The street was excavated for one block down to the level of the tunnel roof. The roof was then built, the street restored above it and the rest of the excavation carried out by tunnelling under the roof. As the Métro was extended, shield tunnelling was used, especially for some of the eight crossings under the Seine. Other crossings were accomplished by the caisson method—sinking giant sections of tube in the river bottom.

Berlin built its first section of the U-bahn from Potsdamer Platz to the Zoological Garden, at the same time Paris was tunnelling under the Champs-Elysées. The German engineers also employed the cut-and-cover technique, but ran into considerably more complicated problems with the waterways as the U-bahn expanded. A bridge over the Spree had to be removed, since the route passed through the foundations of the north abutment and one of the piers. Cofferdams—watertight enclosures partially blocking a waterway—were used here and in some of the crossings of the Landwehr Canal.

But what was destined to become the biggest subway system of all was begun in New York in 1900. Manhattan Island was already the most congested area in the world, and the skyscraper boom was barely beginning. New York was slow to start on subways, despite Alfred Beach's precocious beginning, but once started, the city plunged ahead with truly American vigour. The Interborough Rapid Transit Company was followed at once by the Brooklyn-Manhattan Transit Company, and eventually joined by the city-built Independent Subway. The rapid growth of this enormous system was made possible above all by the conquest of the river problem, thanks to the Greathead-Beach shield. The river crossings did not, however, exhaust the difficulties facing New York's subway builders. Troubles were rich and various. The cut-and-cover method was used, but with complications; the gas mains were raised to street level during construction to prevent explosions. All the same there were accidents. Dynamite was needed to blast through Manhattan rock. On a January day in 1902, a terrific explosion rocked the Grand Central area, killing five people lunching in the Murray Hill Hotel on Park Avenue at 41st Street and injuring nearly two hundred more. A cache of dynamite had been detonated by a fire started by a workman's candle.

In October of 1903, on the west side tunnel in uptown Manhattan, a dozen workmen perished when a delayed series of blasts caught them as they returned to the tunnel heading. Several similar accidents occurred, but the city was more shaken by a spectacular disaster in 1915. Apparently too large a charge was used one morning in the BMT heading just south of Twenty-fifth Street, and some of the timbers supporting the temporary deck overhead were knocked out. The deck slowly caved in, carrying with it a loaded streetcar. Five workmen were crushed to death, and three passengers on the streetcar were killed in the panic.

Three days later an almost identical catastrophe threatened at Broadway, north of Thirty-eighth Street. But this time the streetcar motorman was able to stop in time, halting his car on the very edge of the collapsed deck. Though it was Saturday night in the theatre district, by a miracle only one person was killed.

In February 1916, an incredible repetition occurred of a bizarre accident described in a previous chapter. Three men working in the IRT tunnel under the East River were drawn through the tunnel roof by a sudden blow. Two were killed; the third, Marshall Mabey, shot twenty-five feet into the air above the surface, spun for a moment balanced on a geyser, and plunged back into the river. Despite a broken leg and heavy boots, Mabey swam until a tugboat crew could throw him a rope. He survived to become one of New York's veteran sandhog foremen, even working on the Brooklyn-Battery Tunnel in 1948.

Subways were constructed in one city after another in the years following 1900. The cut-and-cover method was used in nearly all, except for river and canal crossings. Cost of construction, which naturally rises rapidly with growth of a city, has slowed down construction of subways in recent years. Many cities, especially in the United States, wish they had had the foresight to dig subways when the time was ripe.

One underground system which stands out for the number of difficulties encountered is that of Moscow, begun in 1931. The ground under Moscow proved to be extremely variable, with sections of dangerous quicksand. Every method of tunnelling was used, from Paris cut-and-cover to pick-and-shovel digging in sound clay regions, to tunnelling with shield, to sinking pneumatic caissons in quicksand. Despite the problems progress was exceptionally swift due less to the efficiency of technique than to the enormous labour force employed. The Soviet government, then in the midst of its second five-year-plan, backed the underground with an intensive propaganda campaign, recruiting an army of volunteer workers for week-end and after-hours labour. Even visiting foreigners participated as a sort of tourist lark. At the peak of construction on the original system, in May 1934, no fewer than 75,000 workers were engaged on the project.

Today some thirty-odd cities in all parts of the world have underground passenger railways. One city has the unique distinction of possessing a freight subway. Why more cities don't is a mystery; Chicago's little-known underground—even little known to many Chicagoans—has proved an invaluable asset. It came into existence by accident Chicago is one of the truly explosive cities of modern times; in a single generation it grew from a trading post to a city of half a million, and in another twenty years (1880-1900) to a million and a half. The rapidity of Chicago's growth caused the city fathers to seek a more satisfactory solution to the problems of underground communications—telephone and telegraph wires—than the normal one of constantly tearing up the streets to lay new cables. The Illinois Telephone and Telegraph Company proposed to tunnel under the streets, boring a big enough tunnel to hold all the cables the city might need in the future. Like so many engineering ideas of that day, the concept proved a little too grandiose, and after digging twenty miles of tunnels in three years (1900-3) the company went broke. "But from the ashes of this first enterprise," says British tunnel authority Archibald Black, "there arose, phoenix-like, an entirely new idea. The tunnels were sold to a new concern, the Illinois Tunnel Company, and in 1903 an amended franchise was obtained, permitting the tunnels to be used for transportation of merchandise and packages."

The extension of the tunnel into a comprehensive system connecting large commercial buildings with one another and with railroad freight terminals took several years. Tunnelling was done with light air pressure—five to ten pounds—but without shield, since the route lay forty feet deep, in solid blue clay. The oval-shaped heading was six feet wide and seven and a half feet high inside the concrete lining. Tracks are very narrow-gauge—two feet wide. Today there are some 150 electric locomotives pulling over 3,000 cars around the sixty-two miles of tunnel. Unlike passenger subways, this line is built entirely on one level, with no attempt to avoid intersections, of which there are hundreds. But the line, operated by a regular railroad signal system, has never had an accident. Trains are dispatched via a telephone system, and pick up loads not only under but actually inside buildings, for many Loop skyscrapers are equipped with elevators capable of lifting cars to the top or to intermediate floors. Besides merchandise and supplies, many buildings receive coal and dispose of ashes via the underground railroad.

The line is especially useful when a new building is going up or an old one is being torn down. A branch line is tunnelled to the site and the debris of the building shovelled into a chute reaching to the track. Thence it is carried away underground to some point where fill is needed. To the passing observer the extraordinary effect is created of workmen shovelling tons of brick, mortar, and cement into a hole in the ground.

CHAPTER FIFTEEN

Enter, the Automobile

In 1903, while McAdoo and Jacobs were pushing the first Hudson Tube to completion, James H. Whiting, who had made Flint, Michigan, the world centre of carriage-and-wagon manufacturing, hired a petrol-engine inventor named David Dunbar Buick to design a motor suitable for mass production and installation in carriages. Whiting hardly foresaw the future of General Motors, and Charles M. Jacobs and other tunnel engineers hardly foresaw the future of automobile tunnelling. But General Motors was soon turning out cars by the million and the pressure began to build for automobile river crossings, especially in river-bound New York. A bridge-vs.-tunnel debate was settled in favour of a tunnel, authority for which was finally granted in 1919.

The New York and New Jersey Commissions, ancestors of the present Port of New York Authority, later described their next move in these terms:

> The important duty then confronted them [the Commissions] of selecting a Chief Engineer. It was realized . . . that the work was of an unprecedented character and would require the most expert engineering direction.

This assertion, made in an expensive brochure which perhaps marks the beginning of tunnel public relations, is somewhat misleading. The real problem was not who was to direct the operation, but rather whose tunnel plan was to be accepted. Out of many projects, the field had been reduced to two, and considerable acrimony had developed between proponents of the rival plans. One had been advanced by the most illustrious American engineer of the day, General George W. Goethals, whom President Theodore Roosevelt had appointed chief engineer of the Panama Canal. The other was that of a young, rather obscure man, the tunnel engineer of the New York Public Service Commission, First District, Clifford M.

Holland, who had worked on several of the subway tunnels of the past dozen years. A newspaper writer described him as "slim-built, with a bronzed face that needs no second glance to tell that its owner knows a great deal about something, even to a stranger who has never heard of tunnel construction."

Just as in fiction or a melodrama, the slim, bronzed young unknown won out over the famous veteran. But looking back today one cannot resist the temptation to think that possibly justice—or good sense—miscarried. Clifford Holland's design was strictly conventional—twin twenty-nine-foot tubes, wide enough for two lanes each. General Goethal's plan on the other hand called for the enormous tunnel diameter of forty-two feet, within which two levels, each carrying three lanes of cars, would be built. The Goethals plan, oddly enough, would have cost less money, for it was to be built with concrete blocks. Concrete cast in place had proved effective in the Michigan Central tunnel built under the Detroit River 1906-10. The Holland twin tubes would be cast-iron-lined, a much safer method.

Holland claimed, no doubt justly, that the Goethals savings would not be as great as Goethals maintained. Further, Holland and his consultant, W. J. Wilgus, did not think the softer Hudson clay would be held in check by concrete blocks as well as had been the blue clay of the Detroit River. Further, the larger the diameter of an under-river tunnel, the greater the difference in hydrostatic head between the top and bottom of the shield, a problem troublesome enough already. Finally, Holland pointed out that the Goethals roadway width of twenty-two feet six inches provided very insufficient clearance if used for three lanes of autos; his own tubes would carry twenty-foot roadways for two lanes.

But one cannot help saying for the Goethals project that it represented a more realistic approach to the future automobile traffic entering New York across the North River than did the relatively conservative Holland plan. If its defects had been corrected, there can be no doubt that such a six-lane super-tunnel would in the long run have saved the Port Authority enormous sums of money. Vehicular tunnels under the Hudson—and everywhere else—have skyrocketed in costs in the years since.

But even Clifford Holland's tunnel involved a totally new major problem. Where railroad tunnels under the Hudson and East Rivers had proved to be self-ventilating, the rushing trains themselves pushing in an ample supply of air, the automobile created an entirely new hazard. The capacity of each of the twin tubes was over 2,000 vehicles an hour, every one discharging quantities of carbon monoxide. A proportion of one half of 1 per cent of carbon monoxide in the air is lethal.

It was evident from the start that no system depending on injection of air into the tunnel from the portals could meet the problem. A method had to be found for continuous ventilation of the tunnel at numerous points along the way. The system Holland worked out was not so much ingenious as logical. Powerful fans were to force a 60 m.p.h. stream of cold fresh air into a long duct running under the roadway, thence via "expansion boxes" into the tunnel itself in the form of steady breezes. The polluted air meantime could be drawn off on the principle of warm air rising; a duct in the roof of the tube was furnished with numerous openings and with powerful suction fans at the portals. Two huge buildings on either side of the river house the eighty-four fans—"blowers" and "exhausters" —which move the tunnel air.

Of these eighty-four fans, only two thirds or fifty-six, are required for normal operation. The remaining twenty-eight fans are held in reserve for emergencies. Such an emergency arose on May 13, 1947, when a truck loaded with carbon disulphide, a poisonous and inflammable gas, caught fire in the tunnel and exploded. Twenty-three cars were destroyed and sixty persons overcome by the fumes, but all sixty were brought out alive. Despite the ruin of five hundred feet of the tunnel ceiling, traffic was resumed after only fifty-six hours.

Holland, who went to the most painstaking lengths over his ventilation system, actually building a quarter-mile tunnel near Pittsburgh for experimental purposes, did not live to see its operation. While the tunnel was carried on by his assistants Holland went to the sanatorium at Battle Creek, Michigan, in a vain effort to recuperate. His premature death there in 1924, at forty-one, was apparently brought on by overwork—adding his name to the sombre roster of engineering geniuses who gave too much of themselves to their creations. The news of Holland's death cancelled the holing-through celebration. The ceremonial services of President Coolidge, who had pressed buttons before cameras in Washington to fire the holing-through blasts for the Cascade Tunnel and various others, had been enlisted for the under-Hudson tunnel. His failure to press the button on this occasion constituted a solemn mark of respect for the dead engineer.

Holland's successor in charge of the tunnel, Milton Freeman, himself died suddenly, and the tunnel was finally completed by a young engineer named Ole Singstad, who today at the age of seventy-nine is the grand old man of New York tunnelling.

After the Holland

Automotive tunnels have been fewer and less important than might have been imagined. The principal reason is that the problem of constructing bridges over major inland waterways was largely solved at about the time that the need for automobile crossings became imperative.

Here are some important vehicular tunnels following the Holland:

Oakland-Alameda: The George A. Posey Tube, named for the engineer who proposed it, is a single tube built 1925-28, by the trench method, twelve 203-foot sections sunk in San Francisco Bay. At one point during construction the whole tunnel started to slide down towards the middle of the channel, as the soft waterproofing between layers of the concrete lining gave way. After a movement of six inches the slide was checked by jacks.

Detroit-Windsor: Trench system was used here too, but with the steel sections already blanketed in concrete before sinking. Built 1928-30.

Antwerp-Scheldt: Two tunnels, one auto, one pedestrian, were built by the shield method. Though the Scheldt River is not so deep as the Hudson, this tunnel runs deeper than the Holland because the engineers wanted to run it through sound clay, which lay at 116 feet below mean high water. To sink the shafts through the bad ground, the new freezing technique was used—refrigerated brine pumped into the surrounding clay froze it hard, protecting the shafts against water inrushes.

The deep, deep Queensway: The rail tunnel driven under Liverpool's Mersey River in the '80s ran into enough troubles to give pause to subsequent tunnellers. But in the 1920s pressure grew for a highway tunnel, which was undertaken by Sir Basil Mott in 1925. Far less timid than their New York contemporaries, the Liverpool authorities determined on a tunnel diameter of forty-six feet, big enough to accommodate three lanes plus ventilation tubes, two lanes to be built immediately.

Sir Basil, a veteran who had worked under Greathead on the City and South London in the '90s, had to forego compressed air because of the tremendous depth of the tunnel. The Mersey is a deeper river than the Hudson, and the tunnel driven at normal depth below mean high water would have required a pressure of seventy-three pounds per square inch—far more than a man can survive. Sir Basil carried his heading deeper—146 feet below mean high water—into solid sandstone. This porous rock admitted water freely. The solution was to drive a pilot tunnel, from which cement grouting was pumped radially to fill in fissures. The whole job took nine years (1925-34) and remains the most difficult vehicular tunnel yet driven.

Queens-Midtown, New York: On June 26, 1938, during the construction of this pioneer auto tunnel under the East River a fire broke out in the north tube. It was a Sunday, and the watch crew partly flooded the tunnel, but the fire, burning intensely in the compressed air, destroyed the timbering and flooded the whole heading. No one was hurt, and the following week enough air was forced in to permit men to float on rafts to the shield, plug its openings and build a bulkhead.

Shortly after, a blow occurred in the south tube, which filled with water to within nine feet of the roof. But the crew hung on, and engineer Jack Mcdonald and Superintendent Harry Redwood jacked the shield forward two and a half feet, squeezing the ground at the face to make it less porous. It worked; the heading was pumped out, and the tunnel soon finished.

The Three Lincoln Tubes: These companions to the Holland Tunnel, built over a span of twenty-five years, are notable chiefly for their costliness. The two-lane Third Tube, built in the 1950s, cost $95,000,000—slightly more than the first two put together, and nearly double the twin Holland tubes. As in the case of the Holland, a bolder original conception would have proved more prudent in the long run.

The Mont-Blanc: Highway tunnels, like rail tunnels, are not limited to river crossings; they may also pierce mountains.

Several have already done so on a small scale; at present the world's first major vehicular rock tunnel is being driven.

The Mont-Blanc vehicular, discussed for decades, will be finished in 1963—seven and a quarter miles long, the longest highway tunnel in the world. It differs from the great Alpine rail tunnels in one significant respect—instead of being driven by an advance heading and an army of following labourers, it is being drilled and blasted full-diameter. The American machinery used by the French crew drills 140 drill holes thirteen feet deep in five minutes; these are packd with dynamite and fired. On the Italian side of the mountain, hand drills are used with similar results. Were Germain Sommeiller and Alfred Brandt to return to witness the Mont-Blanc operation they would be impressed—but hardly mystified. The process hasn't changed much.

The Mont-Blanc will not retain its title of world's longest vehicular. In the planning stage is a fourteen-mile tunnel under the Brenner Pass between Italy and Austria.

Many other vehiculars will be driven through mountains in the next few years. But the real future of tunnelling lies in another direction.

CHAPTER SIXTEEN

Japanese Tunnel Fever

By the time Simplon II was completed in 1921, engineers regarded hazard as practically a thing of the past in tunnelling. The shield and compressed air had conquered the problem of water-bearing and soft-ground strata. The multiple perils of Alpine tunnelling had been successfully mastered by Brandt and his successors. Certainly no European or American engineer would have hesitated a moment to accept responsibility for driving a heading less than five miles under Takiji Peak on the Izu Peninsula to cut off a loop on the Tokyo-Kobe Railway. The peak was only 2,060 feet above sea level, and rose over only a fraction of the tunnel route, most of which ran no more than seven or eight hundred feet under the ground surface.

The Tanna Tunnel, in fact, commenced by pick and shovel in 1918, had scarcely attracted the notice of engineers when on April 1, 1921, headlines from San Francisco to Bern flashed the news of a stunning disaster—sixteen men killed and seventeen more trapped. Timbering for a distance of 150 feet had given way without warning at a point 980 feet from the east portal. To the handful of Western engineers who knew anything about the Tanna project, the location of the disaster was as mystifying as its occurrence, for it was only on the threshold of the Takiji Peak, at a depth of a few hundred feet.

The Tanna had been authorized as the principal construction feature of the Atami cut-off of the main trunk line of the Japanese Imperial Railway, sixty miles south-west of Tokyo. Since there was no particular urgency, a time span of seven years was allotted, requiring a leisurely progress of 180 feet a month. Work was begun on April 1, 1918, using the Austrian system of a bottom heading followed by enlargement. Poured concrete and concrete blocks were used for the lining. A covered drainage channel was dug in the middle of the bottom heading.

At full width the tunnel was twenty-eight feet wide and twenty-two and a half feet high at the centre of the arch. Since the ground was known to be somewhat doubtful, care was taken with the timbering; green pine logs, fifteen feet long and fifteen inches thick were used. No special effort was made, however, to get the concrete lining in as close as possible behind the advance crew, since the stout timbering seemed secure.

At four in the afternoon of April 1, 1921, by a curious coincidence, the anniversary of the commencement of the tunnel, catastrophe struck. With absolutely no warning, a 150-foot segment of the east heading, close to the portal, gave way with a tremendous crash, immediately burying sixteen workmen and cutting off seventeen others in the advance heading.

As soon as it was ascertained that seventeen men were alive, four separate drifts—small-bore tunnels—were started through the debris. None of these caved in, and the one driven at the top of the old heading reached the trapped survivors in seven days. Though without food, the men had had water, thanks to the inflow, and enough air, since the section of heading in which they were trapped was over half a mile long.

Investigation revealed a "fault"—section of porous ground—of a peculiarly treacherous shape. Only a few inches thick at the bottom of the tunnel, where the heading was being driven, it crossed the tunnel line at an acute angle. But above, it opened out in a wedge; some shock in the hillside mass above had caused the wedge to crumble, bursting the timbering like matchsticks. At the ground surface, a depression was found, twelve by six feet, and three feet deep.

The truth was, the Izu Peninsula represented as hazardous and unpredictable a piece of ground as tunnellers might find on the face of the earth. The whole region was volcanic in origin. Sagami Bay, at the east portal, was the depression crater of a volcanic cinder cone of prehistoric date. Takiji Peak was part of the outer crater wall. Several types of fault rock abounded as well as pockets of soft clay. Furthermore, the peninsula was still subject to earthquakes.

Yet to the tunnel engineers of 1921 it seemed that the accident had been a freak, unlikely to recur. Work was recommenced; a year was required to re-excavate and line the collapsed portion. By the time this work was finished trouble had hit the west heading.

This heading, from the west (Otake) portal, had made satisfactory if slow progress and had reached 4,940 feet when in February 1922, it entered a fault zone about sixty feet deep, bearing a great volume of water under considerable pressure. Nonetheless, it was decided to push ahead, since the heading was still workable. Extra timbering was added. The waterflow suddenly increased; the reinforced timbering cracked and collapsed along a fifty-foot stretch, the tunnel roof sank and fell, tons of debris came piling back behind the fleeing tunnel crew. Yet the flow was controlled and arrested, and the heading again timbered, with the timbering reinforced by concrete.

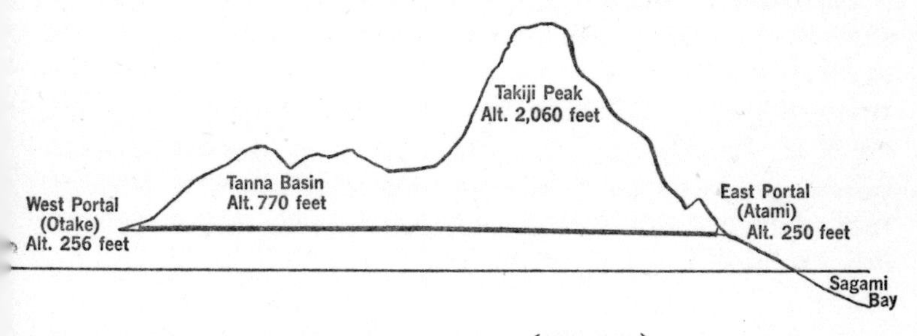

THE TANNA TUNNEL (PROFILE)

Now boulders were encountered; blasting was out of the question in this terrifying terrain. Posts of six-inch steel pipe filled with cement were added to the timbering to resist the mounting ground pressure, but even these buckled.

The bottom heading was halted and a top heading driven to catch up and ascertain the nature of the ground above. This top heading had nearly caught up with the bottom when a torrential stream of water, carrying an enormous volume of earth, burst in; the crew barely escaped by tumbling back into the bottom heading and fleeing for the portal.

The apparently tireless, and certainly dauntless, Japanese engineers now undertook a drift sixty feet south of the main heading. A year was spent bringing this new tunnel up to the point where the main heading had been stopped. Here a heavy water influx stopped the drift. The engineers switched to the other side and explored with anothed drift, which they pushed in two directions. Apparently the ground was safe. Yet on the morning of February 10, 1924, the enlargement of the west bottom heading was underway when a stupendous deluge burst in, rolling in a great wave the whole length of the heading, drowning sixteen men and pouring out the portal in a devastating flood.

The disaster was reminiscent of the Lœtschberg tragedy, but in the case of the Lœtschberg the heading had been passing under a riverbed. Where did the water come from that flooded the Tanna? At this point the tunnel route was 250 feet above sea level and about 500 feet below ground surface. Could a hill of such modest dimensions, on the sea-coast, conceal torrential underground streams?

An extra drainage channel was dug to carry the overflow from the regular channel. It wasn't enough. In September 1924, at 6,900 feet from the west portal, water poured in at the rate of twenty-four feet per second—about 12,000 gallons a minute, equal to the flow that had stopped work in the Simplon. The following March the flow had reached the incomprehensible rate of forty cubic feet per second—18,000 gallons of water every minute, breaking all records of the Simplon or any other tunnel.

A wholly new technique was now applied. A special drainage tunnel, six feet by six feet, parallel to the main tunnel but forty feet from it was undertaken. Its capacity would be 150 cubic feet per second. It was started at once. Before it could be completed the incomprehensible turned into the totally incredible; the flow of water—and sandy debris—suddenly shot up to 123 cubic feet per second, hurling an accumulation of 5,000 cubic yards of debris into the main tunnel. This truly Niagara-like deluge at least found the tunnel workers well alerted and able to escape alive.

Work on the main west heading was stopped at this point in May 1925—7,083 feet from the portal—and all efforts concentrated on the drainage tunnel. It was twelve months before the west heading was advanced. A stretch of 200 feet thus took two and a half years.

Meantime the east heading had been resumed and driven for nearly a mile beyond the point at which work had been stopped due to the disaster of April 1, 1921. In November 1924 the heading pushed into a series of hot springs. Soft clay disintegrated by the hot water virtually flowed into the tunnel; it was all but impossible to hold up enough earth to timber.

When this zone was at last passed the tunnellers hit a "friction-breccia" area where water in moderate volume but under high pressure squirted unpredictably from the blows of the picks. At any given moment a workman might open a hot spring; alarms and accidents became the order of the day. Sometimes not water but hot liquid clay spurted into the faces of the tunnellers. From the beginning of 1924, an advance of 1,000 feet in the east heading took three and a half years. Chief Engineer Fukujiro Hirayama was forced to resort to compressed-air tunnelling, with shield and air-lock. In May 1928 the advance heading passed out of this zone.

The west (Otake) heading had now been advanced by the most exhaustive efforts, including the virtual surrounding of the whole sections with cement, calcium chloride, and sodium silicate, glue-like compounds soluble in water. Again and again water erupted into the heading, sometimes hot, sometimes cold, sometimes more or less clear, sometimes freighted with mud. Drifts were driven all around the heading, bores sunk, springs tapped, in an intricate web of operations by the stubborn tunnellers.

One of the most ingenious involved the use of compressed air and shield to push drifts on opposite sides of the main heading, then withdrawing the air to allow the drift to fill with water. Even this operation was fraught with peril, for the drifts had to be carried into cave zones where sudden loss of compressed air might be feared.

In June 1930 the south drainage drift was suddenly overwhelmed by an inburst of water at eighty cubic feet per second. The drift was abandoned and work begun on another drift on the north side. Meantime work in the main west heading was brought virtually to a standstill.

In the east (Atami) heading similar heroic measures were employed, though the water flow did not achieve quite the proportions of the west heading.

By this time the whole Takiji Peak and especially the Tanna Basin were honeycombed with drainage drifts. Some were driven with compressed air, some by a complicated process of grouting which amounted to squirting cement through pipes into the surrounding fault rock and filling up the fissures through which water was flowing. These drainage drifts were concrete-lined, and where the heading was passing through soft (sofataric) clay they sometimes buckled under the water pressure which they were designed to relieve. But as the drifts drained off the water, the clay around them hardened, and it became possible to advance the main heading. To sustain the terrific ground pressures in the soft-clay zones, the heading was lined with concrete no less than six and a quarter feet thick at the top of the arch, by far the thickest tunnel lining ever constructed.

By the autumn of 1930 it seemed as if every conceivable hazard that could afflict a tunnel had been visited on the Tanna workers. But the Izu Peninsula had a last grim surprise. On November 26, 1930, the whole region was shaken by an earthquake. Five men were buried in the tunnel. Only two were rescued.

Dozens of smaller accidents—from cave-ins of the headings to drownings in the driftways—brought the Tanna toll to nearly seventy, the worst accident record of any tunnel.

In 1931 the east heading progressed only 280 feet; the west heading did not advance at all. In 1932 the east heading gained 996 feet, the waterlogged west remained at a standstill. In 1933 the drifts on the west side at last carried away enough water to permit advancing the main heading—with utmost caution.

The tunnel was finally holed through early in 1934 and completed later in the year. Despite the frightful perils and difficulties which beset it, it was not the longest tunnel in Japan. In 1922, four years after the Tanna was begun, a six-mile rail tunnel was commenced at Shimizu. The two headings met without incident in December 1929—five years before the Tanna.

In the closing years of the tunnel's construction some clues developed on the mystery of where all the water came from. It was noticed that streams and springs around the Tanna Basin were diminishing in flow. Ground water also was found to be depleted. On the other hand, springs around nearby Lake Ashinoko did not diminish, so it was concluded that the water in Tanna could not have come from this source, but must have originated exclusively in the ground water in the immediate vicinity of the tunnel. The mean annual precipitation of the Izue Peninsula is very high, and quite variable, ranging from 1,200 to 2,800 millimetres. This is 47 to 110 inches a year, as compared with forty to sixty inches in well-

DISASTERS CAUSED BY TUNNEL COLLAPSE

(Above) In December 1913 the Chemniz Tunnel, Germany, fell in, burying a train which was passing through

(Above) Twenty people died when a street in the Paris suburb of Clamart suddenly caved in after a rainstorm in February 1961. *(Right)* The cause was a series of forgotten tunnels under the city

Britain's deepest road tunnel, the Mersey Tunnel, was opened in 1934 and remains the most difficult vehicular tunnel yet driven: the junction chamber at Birkenhead

The South Tube of the Lincoln Tunnel built to link Weehawken, New Jersey, with Manhattan Island, nearing completion, April 1937

watered parts of the United States. Most of the rainfall comes in spring and summer, and instead of being evaporated, is absorbed into the porous volcanic surface and sub-surface, to reappear as springs. Thus the Tanna tunnellers were driving through a ground mass riddled with holes which every season were refilled with rainwater.

The famous drainage drifts, constructed with such difficulty and in the face of such hazards, are still functioning. Today the annual rain soaks into the ground as it has for millennia, but much of it, instead of accumulating to return to the surface as springs, escapes through the concrete-lined man-made routes.

Thus passengers on the Tokyo-Kobe line today pass through not only the world's most hazard-ridden tunnel, but through a complex of tunnels—of which all the others are filled with water.

CHAPTER SEVENTEEN

Ahead: Ocean Tunnelling!

It is no great exaggeration to say that the history of tunnelling has consisted in the conquest of two barriers, the river and the mountain. The river was conquered by the shield and compressed air, the mountain by the machine drill and dynamite. The dual conquest, including the invention and trial of these four principal tunnelling weapons and all the main subsidiary tools—cement grouting, ring segments, the air-lock, the pneumatic drill, etc.—may be said to have taken a hundred years, from Richard Trevithick's first attempt to tunnel under the Thames in 1807 to the completion of Simplon I in 1906. By the latter date tunnelling was in a state where no river could thwart the engineers, and no mountain range resist their penetration.

Naturally, we have not attempted in this book to tell the story of every major tunnelling effort. Major tunnels were driven under the Severn and Mersey Rivers in England in the 1870s and '80s with no little difficulty, but we have omitted them because their hazards and solutions were very similar to those of the Hudson and East River tunnellers.

In rock tunnelling, such major United States tunnels as the Moffat in Colorado and the Cascade in Washington State have been omitted for similar reasons. The Cascade Tunnel, longest rail tunnel in North America (seven and three-quarters miles), was driven in less than three years, despite spectacular water inrushes. This tunnel's predecessor, the First Cascade, higher up the mountain, though much shorter (two and a half miles) was a more interesting tunnel. Often it was closed down because of snow on the approaches. Built at the turn of the century, it was operated by steam trains till 1909, and once a harrowing disaster was narrowly averted. An eastbound passenger train, with an extra freight engine hauling, entered the tunnel. The coupling between the regular engine and the auxiliary broke three times inside the tunnel. The excessive smoke from the two locomotives overcame the crew of the regular engine just after the freight engine headed west for help. The conductor, coming forward, was also overcome; so was the brakeman. By this time smoke was filling the whole train. A railroad fireman named Abbot, riding as a passenger, fought his way through to the engine, and released the air brakes. The train rolled backward out of the tunnel, where Abbot, nearly choking, braked it. Numerous passengers were overcome by smoke, but thanks solely to Abbot, not one life was lost.

But with rivers and mountains conquered, is there another barrier for tunnellers to attack? There is indeed. A glance at the globe reveals it. In every part of the world lie ocean straits, narrow but deep bodies of water dividing important land masses. Some of these may be bridged, though the problems of bridge-building in deep water will be complicated by those of averting navigational hazards. But these straits can be tunnelled. The ocean floor is rock, and the great depth at which such tunnelling would have to be carried out therefore has no significance.

One may find on the globe dozens of places where ocean straits and bays interrupt logical transportation lines, and where under-ocean tunnelling carries great promise. Here are some examples.

The English Channel—which we shall take up in the Epilogue of this book.

San Francisco Bay. A four-mile rail tube is already projected, to be built partly by cut-and-cover with prefabricated sections, partly, in the soft ground, by shield.

Chesapeake Bay. A great seventeen-mile bridge-and-tunnel crossing will be constructed, the two tunnel sections, each a mile in length, running under the shipping channels.

Rio de Janeiro Bay. At this writing bids have been sought for a five-mile undersea tunnel.

The Straits of Gibraltar. After the English Channel, this has been for decades the most discussed under-ocean tunnel project. Thomé de Gamond was the first to propose it. With the new development of Africa, it seems certain it will finally be constructed. If so, it will set a new record, for the strait is 200 metres deep.

The Bosporus. This historic strait too has been a frequently mentioned tunnelling site, to link Asia to Europe. The water is very deep, and one suggestion has been a suspended tube, floating one or two hundred feet below the surface.

Bering Strait. Politically as well as economically this may sound far-fetched at present, but the future development of Alaska and Siberia might well bring it about.

The Strait of Messina, between Italy and Sicily.

The Strait of Hormuz, between Iran and Arabia, and the *Bab el Mandeb,* between Arabia (Yemen) and East Africa. Tunnels under these two ancient waterways would permit a short, direct rail line from India and southern Asia to East, South and Central Africa.

The Strait of Malacca, between Malaya and Sumatra. A tunnel here would connect Indonesia with South-East Asia.

Many others might be cited. Above all the list could be almost indefinitely extended merely by suggesting all the possibly desirable tunnel connections within the three great archipelagoes of the Orient—Indonesia, the Philippines, and Japan.

In this last, under-ocean tunnelling has actually already been carried out. This remarkable programme has attracted little attention outside of Japan.

The design of the Japanese Government Railways is to build three under-ocean tunnels to link up the main Japanese island, Honshu, with its three neighbouring islands, Kyushu, Shikoku, and Hokkaido. Of the three straits to be crossed, only one is both narrow and reasonably shallow. This is Kanmon, between Honshu and Kyushu. A tunnel here was proposed as early as 1896. Short though the distance is (two and a quarter miles) it is highly doubtful that the engineers of 1896 could have solved its multiple problems. It was finally begun in 1936; pushed in spite of war, the southbound tube was completed in 1942; the northbound, started in 1940, was finished in 1944. The engineers drew on the extensive tunnelling lore acquired in the Alps, under the Hudson and Mersey, and other places, but above all on their own experience. Japan is one of the most tunnel-conscious places in the world, its relatively small area containing 625 miles of railway tunnels alone.

The most important feature of the engineering work at Kanmon was the driving of a pilot tunnel from both portals. This pilot tunnel served several important purposes. It provided a means of reconnaissance more certain than the vertical borings which had been taken. It furnished a conduit for power and communication lines for the main heading, and a drainage canal, in the fashion of the Tanna drainage tunnels. It was of exceptional importance in the event of encountering either very bad or very good ground. If the ground was bad, the cement-grouting technique of Tanna could be applied —cement squirted under pressure through pipes to completely fill in the bad spot. If the ground was good, extra connecting

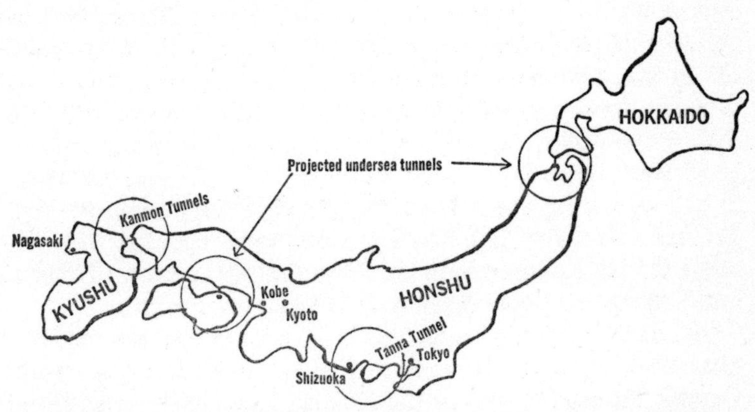

JAPAN'S TUNNELS UNDER THE OCEAN: The two Kanmon tunnels, rail and auto-pedestrian, are already built. Projected are connections indicated between Honshu and Shikoku and Honshu and Hokkaido. Also shown is the Tanna Tunnel, an alternative to which is soon to be built.

shafts to the main heading would make possible the deployment of a bigger work force.

Practically every known tunnelling technique was employed. On the northern approach, it was rock tunnelling. For most of the 1,100 metres under the sea bottom, the same method was used, drilling and dynamiting through solid rock, but with cement grouting to stop water inflows. Under the southern shore shield tunnelling was done, with air pressure up to thirty-seven pounds. For another short section, pneumatic caissons were sunk one after the other and linked up.

In the 1950s a combination highway and pedestrian tunnel was constructed east of the rail tunnel. The highway tunnel, which follows an even shorter route, was built by the same methods and with little difficulty. Thus with a truly Japanese unobstrusiveness, three major firsts in tunnelling were achieved—the first undersea tunnel, the first undersea vehicular tunnel, and the first tunnel in which one can actually walk under the ocean.

The Japanese National Railway is at present intensively exploring the problems involved in the two other major links required to join the four islands in a single rail network. What makes these connections between Honshu and Hokkaido and Shikoku most pressing is the fact that during September and October, Japan is nearly always hit by typhoons from the South China Sea, and ferry service in the straits interrupted. Numerous disasters have occurred. In September 1954, for example, the *S.T. Toya-Maru*, of 4,340 gross tons, and four other ferry boats went down in Tsugaru Strait, between Honshu and Hokkaido, with a loss of 1,448 lives. Another ferry hazard is fog. In May 1955, the *Shiun-Maru*, 1,480 tons, collided with another ship in a dense fog in the Akashi Straits between Honshu and Shikoku and went down with 168 persons aboard.

A tunnel under Akashi Straits is unquestionably feasible, but would have to be executed at an extraordinary depth. Despite the narrowness of the channel (four kilometres, about two and a half miles), the water reaches a maximum depth of 385 feet. On the other side of Awaji Island, in the Naruto Straits, between Awaji and the Shikoku shore, the depth reaches ninety-two feet, though at the narrowest point, formed by two capes, the width is only a little over a kilometre.

Japanese engineers are studying both tunnel and bridge schemes for the crossing. It is even possible a combination might be used—a bridge for Naruto Straits, a tunnel for Akashi.

The biggest Japanese tunnelling project by far, however, is that planned for the Tsugaru Straits between Honshu and Hokkaido. This will be the world's deepest underwater tunnel, and will probably retain the title for a long time to come, for the channel floor along the proposed route lies 140 metres—nearly 460 feet—below the surface. At that, the floor here is part of a ridge, dropping off abruptly to 300 metres. But depth is not itself an obstacle to undersea tunnelling; the question is, how sound is the rock? The Tsugaru soundings have revealed plenty of faults—but these probably can be dealt with by present-day engineers. A pilot tunnel will be driven first, as at Kanmon, and the faults grouted.

The Tsugaru Tunnel will be, as we have noted, bored by the classic cyclical method of mountain tunnelling—drilling, blasting, mucking, ventilating, drilling, etc. There is a possibility that it may be the last tunnel to be so driven. An American company, James S. Robbins and Associates, is currently experimenting with a large-diameter boring machine, capable of driving a tunnel in a single operation, without explosives. Such machinery is of course already used in rock-drilling for oil and other mineral explorations. But creation of an effective and economical machine of a size capable of driving a tunnel bore—say with a twenty-five foot diameter—has until recently been considered impossible. In fact, engineering science had largely fixed its eyes on other possibilities—sonic and ultrasonic "pulsing" with fluorine and other gases. But a few years ago James Robbins happened across an abandoned boring machine in Illinois that started him thinking. The machine was a McKinlay Miner, and Robbins improved it into an effective coal-digging device, the Marietta Miner. Later he improved it further as the Goodman Miner, and eventually, going into business for himself, and adding a disc cutter to his machine, he began a series of tools to bore through soft rock. One was used to tunnel through the shale under the Arkansas River. Another drove a sewer tunnel through Chicago limestone, a third has been performing a similar function in Toronto. Three have been used in the tunnelling work at the Oahe Dam Project in Pierre, South Dakota. Termed "Mechanical Moles" by their builders, these formidable gadgets promise eventually to cut through harder rocks, such as gneiss and granite, with diameters sufficient for vehicular and rail tunnels.

What about that machine James Robbins ran across in Illinois that fathered this formidable series of mechanical monsters? The McKinlay Miner was an American manufacturer's version of a British invention devised in 1881 . . . by a certain Colonel Beaumont, for the British Channel Tunnel Company, Ltd.

The wheel comes full circle; we are back to the Channel Tunnel. In a recent symposium Richard J. Robbins, of Robbins Associates, credited the McKinlay Miner as the forebear of his firm's new machines, and remarked in passing that the original probably would have succeeded in tunnelling under the English Channel if borium and tungsten carbide had been available for the drills. Mr. Robbins is deceived, since the Beaumont machine needed nothing harder than ordinary steel to cut through the chalk under the Channel floor.

That is, provided the Channel floor is chalk, and the chalk is of the right kind, and it extends all the way across the Channel, and provided a few other things are true that the men of 1881 surmised. Only within the last two years have the tantalizing questions of the Channel Tunnel finally been answered.

Epilogue: At Last, the Channel Tunnel

Frank Davidson and Cyril Means are somewhat unusual lawyers. Between Canadian Army service in the war and postwar work with the E.C.A., Davidson has only carried on private law practice briefly since graduating from Harvard magna cum laude. Means similarly has passed most of his time outside the actual practice of law, in the Navy, on the faculty of the Law School at Leland Stanford, as legal adviser to the U.S. High Commissioner for Germany, and as arbitration director of the New York Stock Exchange. Very evidently their unusual backgrounds made them more receptive to the Channel Tunnel than more career-committed lawyers might have been. In any case, after reading Joan Reiter's report on the history and prospects of the Channel Tunnel, the two men looked at each other and said, in effect, Why not?

Davidson was definitely enthusiastic about the idea. Means was a little more sceptical; after all, if the thing was a sound proposition, certainly the British and French would be doing it, wouldn't they? They talked it over with Frank Davidson's brother, Alfred E. Davidson, an investment counsellor and former U.N. official, who immediately added his weight of enthusiasm to that of his brother. Why not at least write to the two old Channel Tunnel Companies and find out if they were still in business?

Means drafted a short letter ("the shortest letter I ever composed") and they sent it off to London and Paris. The letter simply inquired whether there was any interest in American financial support for the Channel Tunnel. The letter to London stirred little reaction at the Channel Tunnel Company, Ltd. The letter to Paris had a quite unexpected result. Davidson's secretary, thanks to Mrs. Reiter's research, found an address for the Société Concessionnaire du Chemin de Fer Sous-Marin in an article published some years earlier in *The Saturday Evening Post:* No. 1, Rue d'Astorg, Paris VIIIe. Though

Davidson and Means didn't realize it, this was the address of the Suez Canal Company. The affairs of the moribund, or hibernating, Société Concessionnaire had been in the hands of a sort of caretaker-secretary who was a full-time employee of the Suez company. By 1956, however, this man had died or gone elsewhere, hardly anyone knew where the office of the Société Concessionnaire was, and the letter presently turned up on the desk of the Director-General of the Suez Canal Company. This was M. Jacques M. C. Georges-Picot, one of the most formidable tycoons in Europe. The curious thing was that, utterly unknown to Means and Davidson, Georges-Picot was himself powerfully interested in the Channel Tunnel.

The situation of the Suez Canal Company for several years had been growing ominous. The ninety-nine-year lease which Ferdinand de Lesseps had obtained from the Khedive of Egypt in 1869 was due to expire in 1968. With the rise of Egyptian nationalism it became more doubtful every year that the concession could be renewed, or rather it became more certain that it could not be. Further, in view of the same political factor, Georges-Picot regarded Egypt as a dubious field for future investment. His hope was to retire unobtrusively from Egypt, extracting as much of the company's capital as possible, and then reinvest in some other major transportation public-works project appropriate to his personnel and organization. He had in fact already brought the Channel Tunnel before his Board of Directors, where he had encountered a solitary objection—from the director representing Her Majesty's Government. This British objection was not based on the time-honoured military factor at all, but on a subtler diplomatic difficulty. The shares which Prime Minister Disraeli had bought in 1875 in Queen Victoria's name from the Khedive of Egypt had always been something of an embarrassment. Governments in general do not care to be mixed up in private enterprise, and where diplomatic complications loom, they are painfully wary. The British government's share in the Suez Canal was 44 per cent, though its voting power was considerably less. But its representatives on the Canal's Board of Directors had been schooled to object on principle to any further international projects of any nature.

Then, in June 1956, Colonel Nasser seized the Suez Canal. In October, just before the Lüchow luncheon, Britain and

France had made an ill-advised attempt to recover the Canal by military means. The result of that venture left the Company higher and dryer than before.

Now, in this difficult situation, Georges-Picot discovered that some Americans were talking about reviving the very Channel Tunnel project that he had been thinking of for years. He at once directed his New York representative to contact Means and Davidson. The Suez Company's interest in the tunnel was duly communicated to Means and Davidson.

The two Americans decided that the only thing to do was to get in direct communication with Georges-Picot. Means had just resigned his position at the Stock Exchange to devote time to an immensely complex copyright case on which he was just starting; consequently, he was free in January 1957 to "run over to Europe for five days" and find out if the Channel Tunnel was really worth any more time and effort.

He was gone five months, returning twice to report. In London he met with a courteous but somewhat restrained reception from Baron Leo F. A. d'Erlanger, Chairman of the Channel Tunnel Company, Ltd., and his associates. But in Paris he had an extremely enlightening series of discussions with M. Georges-Picot. The Suez Company's situation was this:

Around the world, in gilt-edged investments of various kinds, the company had some £50,000,000 in available capital. But its compensation claims against Egypt were running into a stone wall. The company would not care to invest in the Channel Tunnel until these were cleared up, and this might not take place for years. Georges-Picot's position was, why not wait a while? The Channel Tunnel had been waiting a hundred and fifty years already—what harm could three or four more years' delay do?

Means's reply was that he and his friends were not keen on waiting. During the progress of these talks, back in New York Frank Davidson was busy. In Wall Street offices, in panelled club rooms, and at the indispensable luncheon table he succeeded in attracting the interest of enough important financial leaders, including Thomas S. Lamont of J. P. Morgan and Co., to justify forming a corporation. A remarkable French-American engineer who happened to be married to Davidson's wife's sister was brought into the new firm. This was Arnaud de Vitry d'Avaucourt, an honours graduate of the Ecole

Polytechnique, Harvard Business School, and M.I.T., employed as a senior engineer at Socony Mobil. De Vitry became chairman of Technical Studies, Inc., of which Davidson became President and Means Executive Vice-President and Treasurer.

To Georges-Picot, Means suggested that a place be held open for Suez participation at a later date, that meantime Technical Studies and the two old companies go ahead with the necessary surveys.

He repeated this proposal in London, where now interest was definitely rising. Among the old considerations there was a brand-new one in Britain: the European Common Market. The "Inner Six"—France, West Germany, Italy and the Benelux countries—made rapid economic progress in their new grouping. The pressure of their success was quickly felt in the United Kingdom. Britain's future policy was not clear, many businessmen in London and Manchester could not help regarding a rail link to the Continent as a very desirable aid to their competitive position. The Europeans were at first unreceptive to the idea of the surveys. Means informed them that without a competent traffic survey, it would be impossible to sell bonds on the American market. In Britain and Europe one didn't bother with details like traffic surveys. Of course a study had been made in 1930. "I had it done by an ancient clerk who was with us then," d'Erlanger recalled airily. The "ancient clerk" had produced excellent figures, too, which corresponded to the actual statistics on cross-Channel traffic within one or two per cent for all the pre-war years. Means was impressed, but pointed out that even if the "ancient clerk" were still alive, his estimate would carry little weight in American financial circles.

Simultaneously, Georges-Picot either made unexpected progress in his Egyptian negotiations, and felt free to enter at once into participation, or felt that with the enthusiastic Americans plunging ahead, it was now or never. Equally apparently, he had overcome the scruples of Her Majesty's Government to becoming involved in another private-enterprise international public-works project. Indeed, the British government's objections on these grounds would appear illogical, especially since the British government is involved in the project anyway, through the nationalized British railways which own a large share of the British Channel Tunnel Company. In May d'Erlanger made it official with an announcement at a meeting of shareholders of the British company. A study group was being formed with equal participation (25 per cent) for each of the old tunnel companies and for the Suez Company, with 10 per cent reserved to Technical Studies, Inc., it being understood that the American company could later increase its share and become an equal partner, with each of the four interests holding 25 per cent. This, in fact, occurred, shortly, when Technical Studies, with funds invested by Morgan, Stanley and Co., Dillon, Read and Co., Thomas S. Lamont and American Research and Development Corp., supplied funds for a programme of core borings in the Channel.

What emerged was a Channel Tunnel Study Group, empowered to spend some £75,000 on a double-barrelled survey of the traffic expectations and the geology of the Channel bottom. Various highly specialized consultants and experts, British, French, and American, were employed. De Leuw, Cather of Chicago were brought in for the traffic survey, in collaboration with a British and a French firm. Traffic surveys and forecasts are a far more American than European custom, as Means had learned; an interesting outgrowth of the whole American involvement in the Channel Tunnel, in fact, is a sharp stimulus to European traffic research.

The compact report produced by the Channel Tunnel Study Group is dated March 28, 1960. It asserted that "the economic and military arguments which, until recently, threw doubt on the desirability of a tunnel . . . have now lost much of their force," and that "with modern methods of construction the Channel Tunnel is technically and financially feasible." The tunnel which the Study Group considered most practicable was a double-track rail tunnel capable of passing 1,800 vehicles a hour under the Channel on specially made flat cars.

The studies themselves were supervised by two eminent engineers, René Malcor, chief engineer of Bridges and Roads for the French Government, and H. J. B. Harding, vice-president of the London Institution of Civil Engineers, and were divided into five sections: traffic survey, geological study, engineering study, financial study, and legal study. The five-headed report provides an admirable picture of the English Channel Tunnel, its problems, its probable solutions, and its bright prospects.

First of all, how much traffic can be anticipated: Going over the ground covered by the various studies of 1930, the new group concluded that a rail tunnel would in 1965 carry over 3,000,000 persons a year, over 600,000 automobiles and trucks, and over 1,250,000 tons of freight. By 1980 the totals would reach almost 5,000,000 persons, over 1,000,000 vehicles and 1,500,000 tons of freight.

Charges would not necessarily have to run below those of competing air and ferry lines, but the study group calculated that on the basis of the traffic forecast, reductions of 5 per cent on passenger-ferry charges, and of 30 and 50 per cent on vehicles and freight could be made. The fare would thus be a trifle over 30s. per passenger and less than £5 per car. The freight rate would be about £2 per ton.

Consideration was also given to a highway tunnel. Contrary to what one might expect, the foreseeable passenger and even auto traffic through a highway tunnel would be below that on a rail tunnel, and freight carried would amount to only about a third.

The reason for this advantage for the rail tunnel lay in the following calculations: With traffic moving at 35 m.p.h., a two-lane highway tunnel would have a peak capacity of 1,300 vehicles an hour in both directions. The railway's specially constructed side-loading cars would traverse the tunnel at 60 m.p.h. Using only single-decked cars, the capacity of the rail tunnel would be 1,800 cars per hour in each direction. If the cars were double-decked this figure could be doubled. Thus despite delays of loading and unloading, which would be minimized by careful planning at the terminals, the car-carrying trains could convey several times as many automobiles and passengers through the tunnel as could pass through on a road surface.

These calculations are based, of course, on the old-fashioned railway. In the perhaps not too distant future, for just such projects as the English Channel Tunnel, may be envisioned "futuristic" schemes like the Ford Motor Company's Levacar, designed to travel just above rather than on rails, at speeds of 125 to 400 m.p.h.

What about a combined road-and-rail tunnel? It will be recalled that André Basdevant, the French engineer who interested S.H.A.P.E. in the tunnel in the 1950's, was a protagonist of a combined tunnel. The Basdevant scheme has an unquestionable fascination. A single tube of gigantic bore, it would carry a four-lane highway divided by an island, running above a two-track railway. Basdevant would construct this enormous tunnel by driving a pilot heading at the bottom of the diameter, and enlarging from this pilot heading while using it for the removal of detritus, which might be accomplished simply by flooding from the middle of the tunnel.

Serious engineering objections had been raised to Basdevant's heady proposal before the Channel Tunnel Study Group considered it. The ventilation problem for a four-lane highway thirty-two miles long would be terrific, to say the least. Above all, it is extremely doubtful that a tunnel of so large a bore could remain within the grey chalk. This question would complicate an already excessive cost factor for such a tunnel.

The Channel Tunnel Study Group estimated that a two-track rail or two-lane highway tunnel can be constructed at a total cost, including approaches and necessary installations, of about £100,000,000. A combined highway-and-rail tunnel, smaller than that envisioned by Basdevant, with only a two-lane highway, would cost over £170,000,000. Considering the anticipated revenue—£20,000,000 by 1980 for the rail tunnel, £12,000,000 for the highway—the rail tunnel had a clear economic advantage. The Study Group made no estimate of the revenue from a combined tunnel, evidently regarding it as only slightly larger than that anticipated from a rail tunnel alone. Assuming this to be the case, it is clear that the cost would make private financing out of the question. Such a tunnel, if it could be built at all, would simply take too long to pay for itself. Basdevant's design might have been less visionary as an immersed tube, since the geological risk would then be eliminated.

The Study Group recommended that private financing to the extent of about £100,000,000 be undertaken to start the project. This would cover the actual cost of construction of the tunnel, leaving the terminals and rolling stock to be financed by the railways. But if either government so desires, the tunnel company would undertake additional financing for the terminal facilities. The Study Group recommended the formation of an international company, created by a French-British treaty, the company to be granted a ninety-nine-year concession.

But the most interesting portion of the Study Group's report deals with the geology of the Channel. Explorations, as we have seen, had been carried out for over a hundred years, beginning with Thomé de Gamond's Sunday excursions, or rather even earlier, for Mathieu and Mottray, the tunnel's very first advocates, had had good knowledge of the sea floor. As we have noted, the maximum depth in the Straits of Dover is 180 feet. Furthermore, the drop is abrupt on both shores, so that the floor is quite level all the way across. The two well-known ridges, the Varne Bank and Le Colbert Ridge, lie south of the tunnel route, which runs north-west from Sangatte, dipping in a slight curve to the south, entering Shakespeare Cliff directly in front of Dover and turning sharply south to Folkestone.

A most intensive examination of the sea floor was undertaken, for Davidson, Means, and their associates hoped to avoid the costly necessity of a pilot tunnel. Remarkable new techniques were available. One was sonar, used to detect submarines, and also for oil prospecting under the sea. Sonar penetrates the sea floor to a distance of about a hundred feet, giving an excellent picture of the various strata.

The sonar investigation was carried out in 1958; the following summer a still newer instrument, the "sparker," was employed. This device, which is operated by only two (American) companies in the whole world, penetrates the sea bottom hundreds of feet. The operation was directed by Walter C. Beckman, head of Alpine Geophysical Associates, Inc., a firm in New Jersey which is actually a sort of offshoot of Columbia University. Mounted in a forty-two-foot British vessel formerly used for air-sea rescue work, the sparker produced an extraordinarily complete picture of the tunnel floor along the Sangatte-Folkestone route, where the Lower (grey) Chalk was known to extend. In addition, several deep boreholes were made, including one of 814 feet at Escalles in France, and three shallower ones in the Dover-Shakespeare Cliff region in England.

The combined methods made possible a complete hydrographic map of the Straits of Dover. Some gravel-filled gulleys appeared, one of them running 279 feet down.

The investigation was far from over, however. Frogmen were sent to the bottom to bring back samples of the floor; these were subjected to microscopic analysis. Finally, eight borings were made in the seabed itself. This was an extremely tricky operation. The boring boat had to be held absolutely steady in the Channel current. First a large-diameter guide tube was lowered to the sea floor. In this was inserted the drill tube. After the drilling and extraction of the sample, the drill hole was filled in with concrete—so that when the tunnel heading came along it wouldn't suddenly hit an open connection with the sea.

What were the results of this exhaustive research? In the words of the report, they "confirm the conclusions drawn from the 1875-76 operations regarding the continuity of Cenomanian or Lower Chalk formation and show that its thickness varies from 262 feet on the English coast to 213 feet on the French coast. Three pockets of gravel and some unfilled gullies were identified as well as slight faults orientated parallel to the line of a possible tunnel. But no faults crossing this alignment at right angles were detected.

The Study Group also examined the Jurassic route, farther south, which would pass under the Varne Bank and the Colbert. This route was favoured by André Basdevant for his road-rail tunnel, since it would permit use of the two banks for construction of artificial islands, helping to solve the ventilation problem. But the Study Group declared that a tunnel in this region, outside the Lower Chalk area, would run in widely varying ground, including probably a number of rock faults. The presumption would be that a pilot heading would have to be driven and radial grouting injection resorted to—feasible, but very costly. Compressed-air work would be out of the question at such a depth.

Thus, everything appeared to be settled: the route, Sangatte to Folkestone, in order to keep within the Lower Chalk; the type of tunnel, two-track rail, for economic reasons; the method of construction, machine boring, by what was essentially an improved version of Colonel Beaumont's famous Victorian gadget. Experiments showed that a machine with a diameter as large as twenty-four feet could advance through grey chalk at 1,475 feet per month. From two headings this would amount to seven miles a year, or a little over four years for the total distance. The tunnel would be lined with concrete, not for support, which would be unnecessary, but to protect the electrical equipment against damage from seepage.

But during the course of its investigations the Study Group discovered that there is an entirely different method for tunnelling the Channel which is perfectly practicable today. The Study Group calls it the "immersed tube" method, and it is nothing more nor less than old-fashioned "build-and-sink," or "trench tunnelling," first used for the Michigan Central Railroad Tunnel at Detroit back in 1906. It had always been assumed that build-and-sink was inapplicable to the Channel because of the depth and the turbulence. But in the late 1950s

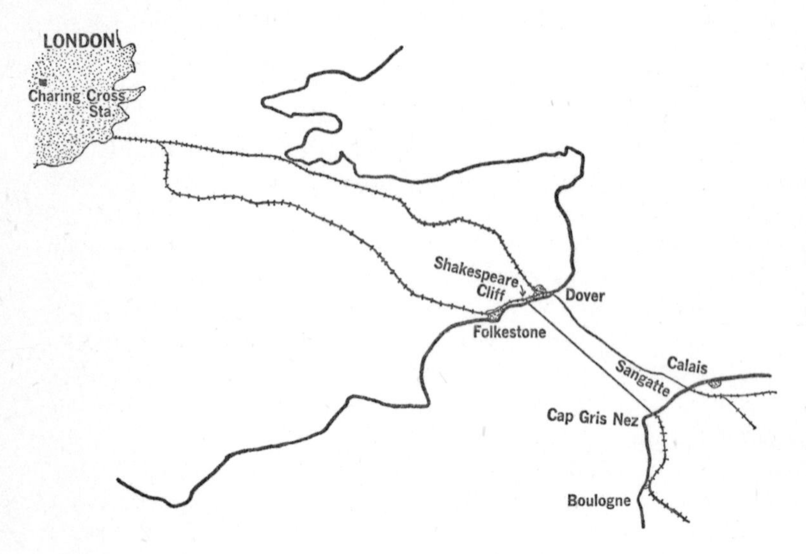

TWO ROUTES FOR THE ENGLISH CHANNEL TUNNEL: Straight-line route is for an immersed tube; alternative is for a bored tunnel, which would have to follow changing pattern of chalk layer.

this method was actually used with outstanding success on the Hyperion Outfall. This gloriously named work is a sewage conduit built out into the Pacific Ocean by the city of Los Angeles. It runs five miles into the ocean at a depth of 207 feet —twenty-seven feet more than the deepest level in the Straits of Dover. The construction was made possible by the "Texas Tower"—a remarkable sea-going platform on stilts developed by the De Long Corporation. The Texas Tower navigates to its destination, then lowers its "legs"—a number of stilt-like supports which reach down to the ocean floor and then elevate the whole vessel completely out of the water. Working operations are then carried on from this solid and stable platform, undisturbed by the roaring torrent below.

The engineers backing the immersed-tube plan calculate that they can build the tunnel slightly cheaper than can be done by boring. Doubts have been raised on this point. A Texas Tower might stand firm enough in the Channel to permit lowering of a tunnel segment and locking it in place, but what about the next step—moving to a new position? In rough weather, could the tower be navigated with enough precision to enable it to centre accurately after once drawing up its legs?

Colonel L. B. De Long, the colourful Texan who heads the De Long Corporation, was asked about this repositioning problem. His response was a remarkable piece of off-the-cuff engineering genius. "Why hell, we'll just build one like a slide rule," he said, and taking paper and pencil immediately diagramed for his edified hearers a new type of platform with side panels attached. The sides would carry their own legs; when it was time to move, the main platform would be held in place while the side platforms drew up their legs and were driven forward half or three-quarters of a length. Their legs would then be lowered firmly on bottom again, the legs of the main platform raised, and the main platform brought forward to the new position, flush with the sides. This great geometric primate would stilt-crawl its way from Gris Nez to Folkestone, cutting a trench in the bottom and lowering the segments of steel tube into place.

So evenly matched are the two methods—full-diameter boring and build-and-sink—that even at this late date neither has won an advantage. The British and French governments may decide, possibly on the basis of a sort of defence consideration of a new kind. The bored tunnel, lying some distance under the sea floor, would obviously be more immune to destruction than the trench tunnel.

"On the other hand," says Davidson cheerfully, "they may simply toss the ball back to the Study Group. In which case we'll have to make up our minds."

When will construction actually begin? And when will the tunnel be open?

What the tunnellers are presently waiting for is conclusion

of the formal Franco-British Treaty establishing the status of the company. This treaty has been under intensive study by the various bureaus of the French and British governments, and may be signed by the time this appears in print. In that case, work could begin in 1963, and you may pass under the English Channel, riding in a comfortable Pullman coach, with your car on a truck behind you, by the end of 1966. The cost will probably be about £9 for car and family.

There is something anticlimatic about the English Channel Tunnel. Partly, perhaps, the subject is a little tired after so much exercise. In *The Stone of Chastity*, novelist Margery Sharp has a young M.P., "so young that he was still constantly looking for audiences to address," one of whose regular subjects is the Channel Tunnel. The implication is that already in 1939 one didn't mind the Channel Tunnel except that hearing about it was a bit of a bore.

Today it is as if a pleasant buffet has been left on the sideboard while the party was postponed for several days. Even the news that Field-Marshal Montgomery opposes the tunnel stirs only yawns in the London Press.

But more than this, the truth is that tunnelling the English Channel has always been considerably overrated. It actually could have been driven in the 1880s—at a time when tunnelling under the Hudson River was a problem that baffled solution, and when even the most daring Alpine engineers shrank from the Simplon. It could have been done with ease in the 1930s—a time when the Japanese, after unheard-of disasters and hardships, were finally finishing the Tanna and hardily beginning the Kanmon.

The Channel Tunnel will be large, it is true, but so far from being difficult, it will be one of the easiest major tunnelling jobs ever undertaken. The very division of attention between traffic studies and engineering problems reveals the extent to which daring has been replaced by calculation. The heroes of the story are a couple of imaginative American lawyers who have never passed through an air-lock, or seen water shoot from a drill hole.

The romance, of course, is not altogether gone from tunnelling. Hazard remains, men can still lose their lives. Problems remain; engineers still invent new tricks, like Colonel De Long's sea-going slide rule. There is something quite engaging about the little boatload of sparker technicians bobbing about in the Channel shipping lanes and taking soundings of the strata far beneath the bottom of the sea. And in a quite real sense tunnelling's great days lie in the future, in the construction of the secure, all-weather routes for passengers and freight under the straits of the world.

Yet one cannot help concluding that the twentieth century, with its cornucopia outpouring of scientific and engineering tools and techniques, has overwhelmed the challenge of the tunnel. What engineer of the future will have himself awakened every two hours at night to be shown samples of the ground through which his tunnel is passing, as Marc Brunel did during the Thames Tunnel construction? Who in this tax-ridden century will spend his own funds—and invent an important new tool—to dig a purely experimental tunnel, merely by way of showing that it can be done—as did Peter Barlow in London and Alfred Beach in New York? What engineer, contractor, or government will plunge into the biggest tunnelling job ever undertaken by man on the strength of a belief that a wholly new, untried, in fact not even yet created, tool and technique, will work—as did Germain Sommeiller and the Piedmontese government in Mont-Cenis in 1857?

Perhaps the quality that is gone is mere recklessness, and perhaps engineering is better off without it. But what a history it made!

BIBLIOGRAPHY

GENERAL:

The Story of Tunnels, by Archibald Black. Whittlesey House, New York, 1937. (This book, the only general popular work on tunnelling in English, is no longer in print.)

Eminent Engineers, by Dwight Goddard. Hill Publishing, New York, 1905.

Famous Bridges and Tunnels of the World, by H. A. Hartley. Globe Books (Frederik Muller), London, 1956. (Juvenile.)

Great Engineers, by Prof. C. Matschoss, trans. by Dr. H. Stafford Hatfield. G. Bell and Sons, London, 1939.

Famous Subways and Tunnels of the World, by Edward and Muriel White. Random House, New York, 1953. (Juvenile.)

MISCELLANEOUS:

NEWSPAPERS: *The New York Times, Figaro, The Brooklyn Daily Eagle,* etc.

MAGAZINES: *This Week Magazine, The Rotarian, The Saturday Evening Post, Paris Match, Scientific American, Leslie's Weekly, American Review of Reviews, American Hetitage,* etc.

Brochures, booklets, information, maps, etc., from the Port of New York Authority, the Swiss National Tourist Office, French Information Service, British Information Service, Japanese Consulate in New York, British Travel Association, New York Board of Water Supply, British Institution of Civil Engineers, New York Historical Society, etc.

Encyclopedia Britannica, Britannica Yearbook, Rand-McNally Atlas, Dictionary of American Biography, The Blue Guide, Encyclopedia Americana, various almanacs, etc.

REFERENCE:

Channel Underground, by Deryck Abel. Pall Mall Press, London and Dunmow, 1961.

"Notes on the Construction of the East River Gas Tunnel," by Walton I. Aims, C.E. Read before the Boston Society of Civil Engineers, April 17, 1895.

Les grands souterrains transalpins, by Charles Andreae. Leemann Frères, Zurich, 1948.

Problèmes du projet et de l'établissement de grands souterrains routiers alpins, by Charles Andreae. Leemann Frères, Zurich, 1949.

"Geophysical Surveying for a Channel Tunnel," by Walter C. Beckmann. *The New Scientist*, March 24, 1960.

Tunnelling by Machinery, Devised by Herman Haupt, Paris Exposition of 1867, by Blanchard and McKean. H. C. Leisenring's Steam Printing House, Philadelphia, 1867.

A History of Egypt, by James Henry Breasted, Ph.D. Charles Scribner's Sons, New York, 1909.

Memoirs of Sir Marc Isambard Brunel, ed. by Richard Beamish. Longman, Green, Longman, and Roberts, London, 1862.

Modern Tunneling, with Special Reference to Mine and Water-Supply Tunnels, by David W. Brunton and John A. Davis. John Wiley, New York, 1914.

Tunneling under the Hudson River, by S. De Vere Burr. John Wiley, New York, 1885.

"The St. Gothard Tunnel," by S. H. M. Byer. *Harper's New Monthly*, vol. 57, no. 341, October, 1878.

"The Rome Metropolitan Railway," by C. Carty, Dipl.-Ing. *The Engineer* (London), February 8 and 15, 1952.

The Channel Tunnel, London and the Tunnel, etc., papers and addresses, printed by McCorquodale and Co., London, 1918.

"The Channel Tunnel Study Group," report, March 28, 1960.

"The Tanna Tunnel," by W. Harvey Clarke, Jr. *The Far Eastern Review*, May, 1933.

"The Great Tunnels of the World," by Charles W. Comstock. Proceedings of the Colorado Scientific Society, Vol. VIII, pp. 363-86, Denver, 1908.

"The Loetschberg Tunnel," by E. L. Corthell, M. Am. Soc. C.E. *Engineering News*, Vol. 65, No. 1, January 5, 1911.

Tunnel Shields and the Use of Compressed Air in Subaqueous Works, by William Charles Copperthwaite. Van Nostrand, New York, 1906.

The World Beneath the City, by Robert Daley. J. B. Lippincott, Philadelphia and New York, 1961.

"Evolution of Rapid Transit Facilities," an address by J. Vipond Davies, Consulting Engineer, at the annual dinner of the Chamber of Commerce of Pittsburgh, November 25, 1912.

"The Tunnel Construction of the Hudson and Manhattan Railroad Company," by John Vipond Davies. Proceedings of the American Philosophical Society, Vol. XLIX, No. 195, 1910.

"Difficult Mountain Railway Construction in Switzerland," *Engineering News, December* 19, 1901.

St. Columba and the River, from Chains, by Theodore Dreiser. Boni and Liveright, New York, 1927.

Tunneling, Explosive Compounds, and Rock Drills, by Henry Sturgis Drinker. John Wiley, New York, 1878.

Engineering News-Record, Vol. 84, No. 13, March 25, 1920.

Tunnels, Underground Structures, and Air-Raid Shelters, by A. A. Eremin. Sacramento, 1958.

Le Percement du Mont-Cenis, by Louis Figuier. Typographie Lahure, Paris, 1872.

"Seven Modern Wonders Named," by J. Jip Finch, A.S.C.E. *Civil Engineering,* November, 1956.

The Subways and Tunnels of New York, by Gilbert H. Gilbert, Lucius I. Wightman and W. R. Saunders. John Wiley, New York, 1912.

"Underground Electric Railways in London: The City and South London Railway, with some remarks upon subaqueous tunnelling by shield and compressed air," by James Henry Greathead, M. Inst. C.E., with an abstract of the discussion upon the paper, ed. by James Forrest, secy. Excerpt Minutes of Proceedings of the Institution of Civil Engineers, Vol. cxxiii, session 1895-96, part i, London, 1896.

(James Henry Greathead. Obituary.) Institution of Civil Engineers, Minutes of Proceedings, Vol. 127, London.

Tunnel Engineering, by Rolt Hammand. Macmillan, New York, 1959.

(Herman Haupt. Obituary.) *Railway Gazette,* December 22, 1905.

Shield and Compressed Air Tunneling, by B. H. M. Hewett and S. Johannesson. McGraw-Hill, New York, 1922.

New York State Bridge and Tunnel Commission: Design of Cast-Iron Tunnel Ring, submitted to the Board of Consulting Engineers by C. M. Holland, chief engineer. 1921.

Les Misérables, by Victor Hugo, trans. by Charles E. Wilbour, Grosset and Dunlap, New York.

Chief Engineer's General Report Upon the Initiation and Construction of the Tunnel Under the East River, New York, by Charles M. Jacobs. New York, 1894.

"The Hudson River Tunnels of the Hudson and Manhattan Railroad Company," by Charles M. Jacobs, with discussion. Excerpted from the minutes of the Proceedings of the Institution of Civil Engineers, London, 1910.

"Construction of Hokoriku Tunnel," Japanese National Railways, 1959.

"Kammon Undersea Tunnel," Japanese National Railways, 1958.

"Planning for Construction of Inter-Island Through Railways Connecting Honshu with Hokkaido and Shikoku," Japanese National Railways, 1958.

"Japanese Railways at a Glance," Japanese Railway Engineering, July 1959, No. 1.

"Undersea Tunnels in Japan," by Akira Kanatani. Japanese Railway Engineering, Vol. 1, No. 5, December, 1960.

"The Loetschberg Tunnel," by H. Prime Kieffer. *The Railroad Age Gazette,* July 2, 1909.

Les Grands tunnels des Alpes et du Jura, by James Ladame Dubuisson, Neuchatel and Paris, 1889.

"Lincoln Tunnel Third Tube," *The North American Fieldman,* Vol. 13, No. 7, August-September, 1956.

"Tunnels of Classical Antiquity," an unpublished paper by Cyril C. Means, Jr.

"1919-30 Report on the Holland Tunnel," New York State Bridge and Tunnel Commission reports, 1907-30.

"The Railway Tunnels of New York City," by Alfred Noble, C.E., L.L.D., Consulting Engineer, New York City. Reprinted from the *Journal of the Franklin Institute,* April 17, 1895.

The Brunels, Father and Son, by Celia Brunel Noble. Cobden-Sanderson, London, 1938.

Protective Construction Symposium, 2nd, March 24-26, 1959; Proceedings (Deep Underground Construction), comp. by. J. J. O'Sullivan. Rand Corporation, Santa Monica, 1959.

Papers on the Hoosac Tunnel (a collection bound in one volume by the Engineering Societies Library).

Persona and Organizations of Interest in Connection with the Channel Tunnel Project, 1957-60.

Sandhog, Journal of the American Medical Association, Vol. 159, No. 8, October 22, 1955.

Practical Tunnelling, by Frederic Walter Simms. C. Lockwood, London, 1877.

The Channel Tunnel, by Humphrey Slater and Correlli Barnett. Allan Wingate, London, 1958.

The Lives of the Twelve Caesars, by Suetonius, ed. with notes by Joseph Gavorse. Modern Library, New York, 1931.

"The Channel Tunnel Project, an account of the 1959 Sea Bed Investigations," by M. J. Tomlinson, M.I.C.E., A.M.I. Struct. E. and R. F. Heynes, B.Sc. (Eng.), A.M.I.C.E. Reprinted from The Dock and Harbour Authority, February, 1960, Vol. XL, pp. 317-21.

Vom Bau des Simplontunnels, 1898-1921, zur Feier der Schlussteinlegung im Tunnel II, 4 Dezember, 1921. Paul Attinger, Neuchatel, (No Date).

INDEX